SELF-CARE
FOR THE
CREATIVE

A SURVIVAL GUIDE
FOR CREATIVES,
EMPATHS AND HIGHLY
SENSITIVE PEOPLE

STEFANI FRYZEL

Printed in the United States of America

Hardcover ISBN: 978-1-960876-11-9
Paperback ISBN: 978-1-960876-12-6
Ebook ISBN: 978-1-960876-13-3

Library of Congress Control Number: 2023939876

Muse Literary
3319 N. Cicero Avenue
Chicago IL 60641-9998

Advance Praise for
Self-Care for the Creative

"Chock full of important and easy to implement strategies, Fryzel is to creatives what Brené Brown is to leaders. A must read (and apply) for anyone devoted to a sustainable, successful, creative life!"
—Sara Connell, bestselling author of *The Science of Getting Rich for Women* and founder of Thought Leader Academy

"A fun, relatable, easy-to-read survival guide for the highly sensitive, empathetic creative. Full of sage advice and wisdom that traditionally can only be learned the hard way. Stefani saves you the trouble, sits you down like a big sister would, and spells out a step-by-step program of practical solutions to the obstacles you will surely face on your creative journey. I wish I had access to these tools early in my career!"
—Bonnie McKee artist, award-winning filmmaker, and Grammy nominated cowriter of 10 #1 Billboard Hot 100 Hits

Dedicated to the dreamers
brave enough to fucking go for it.

(and to my cousin, Crestina)

Acknowledgments

Jen Sincero. Your book proposal program gave me the confidence I needed to believe that I could write a book in the first place. Thank you for creating something that holds the hands of new writers, while simultaneously evoking the badassery we need to see it through.

Sara Connell. You and Thought Leader Academy have changed my life and made writing my first book become a reality. Coaching with you has been the ultimate divine download. Thank you for being the example I needed to see in my life in order to believe more for me is possible.

Thank you, Audrey Fierberg. Editing my manuscript with you helped turn me into an author. Thank you for helping me find my magic as a writer.

To Libby and everyone at MUSE Literary. Thank you for your time, attention, and care in this project. I'm forever grateful.

To my assistant, Jazzy Luchini. Thank you for helping me launch this book. You are the reason why I now feel like Superwoman.

A special thank you to all the book contributors. Thank you for sharing your stories with the world.

Disclaimer

This self-care book is intended to offer guidance, support, and inspiration for enhancing your overall well-being and personal growth. It is not a replacement for professional therapeutic or medical advice.

If you are struggling with severe mental illness, emotional distress, or any condition that requires clinical assessment and treatment, we strongly urge you to seek the assistance of a qualified therapist, doctor, or psychologist.

While this book can provide valuable insights and strategies for self-improvement, it is essential to prioritize your mental and physical health. This resource should complement, not substitute for, the care and expertise of trained professionals who can address your unique needs.

Your well-being is of utmost importance, and we encourage you to take the necessary steps to ensure you receive the appropriate assistance and support.

Contents

It's a Self-Care Emergency

It's to the point where at the end of most days, you're hoping a glass of wine is enough to knock you into a coma. You're exhausted and overwhelmed. You're juggling a million moving parts (again). Switching gears and switching hats faster than a racecar driver who owns a lot of hats. Your gas tank is empty. There's no time to catch your breath, let alone hear your own thoughts. Your brain feels disconnected. Your body feels like a fucking sandbag. Your schedule is packed, but your creative well is drying up. Still, you tell yourself to put on your big girl pants and just "get through it." You forgot to eat breakfast, switch the laundry, and call back your friend. You can't even remember the last time you ate. Does food taste like anything anymore?

Your anxiety has been at an all-time high. You've been plagued with writer's block, depression, and panic attacks, feeling misaligned with your purpose and just wanting to give up. Now you're fighting tears, unable to decode *any* of your emotions because you haven't made time to feel them. Stress-mode has fully invaded your castle, totally wrecking the vibe of your inner Queendom. There are some ugly gremlins (you know, those paralyzing, self-sabotaging beliefs) sitting on your throne instead of you, kicking around your gorgeous crown while your soul drowns in the moat.

Staying on top of everything is *Mission: Impossible.* Why are there so many freaking things to do in life? It already takes *sooo* much to manage a career, to be creative, to be

SELF-CARE FOR THE CREATIVE

an entrepreneur (oh! and a social media guru)—all while breaking boundaries and glass ceilings *on top* of being a good friend, sister, daughter, mother, wife, coworker, cook, cleaner, bill-payer, errand-runner, mental laborer, and so on. There's never enough time for anything, and the things you really want to be doing (like taking a nap or going on more "artist dates"), you aren't doing because you've convinced yourself that being a professional juggler of a thousand flying balls 24/7 is more noble than taking care of yourself. What's worse, you've also told yourself that if even just one of these balls hits the ground, you're a complete and utter failure.

Sometimes our approach to self-care (or lack thereof) can be a bit like boarding a plane without any safety checks. That thing is gonna crash. When you give everyone and everything else a first-class ticket to your time, effort, and attention, and there's no concept of putting on your own oxygen mask first before helping others, then I'm sorry to say, your flight time is a short duration to Destination: Overwhelm and Burnout.

Remember the movie *Final Destination*? The one where Devon Sawa's character has a premonition that the airplane is going to explode and he wakes in a frantic sweat, trying to warn all the passengers that the plane is indeed going to combust and kill everyone on board? Understandably, most people think he's crazy, and the crew ushers him off the plane. Everyone else stays put except a couple of his friends who believe him, at least enough to disembark with him. Remember that?

Well, let me be Devon Sawa's character for a moment and give you a short preview of your own tragic death if you choose to board the same plane without actually doing any real self-care or any safety checks. The plane will take flight. The engine will fail. There will be a giant explosion in the sky. And a million pieces of disintegrated airplane will rain down toward the earth as you perish in flames. That's not what Katy Perry meant when she said, "Baby, you're a firework."

Girl. Get the fuck off that plane, before you fucking die.

I'm a Prepper

I live in Los Angeles. A high risk hazard zone for earthquakes. In my spare closets I have forty gallons of water, a month's supply of food, flashlights, a hand-crank radio, first-aid kits, go bags, a trunk full of tools and supplies, and enough candles for a forty-day seance. My level of preparedness is borderline nuts enough to go on the show *Doomsday Preppers* (love that show, btw), minus the guns and a bunker. I realize the level of lunacy that occurs on that show, but I still find myself saying in agreement, "He's got a point." For whatever reason, I was raised to think ahead and always be prepared for every possible worst-case scenario. If the power goes out, backup generator. If you've got boo-boos, I've got some Band-Aids. If you've got shattered windows, I've got a tarp and a nail gun. If you go missing, I've probably even got photos of you on deck, ready to deploy the search team. At my core, I'm a prepper who's thinking ten steps ahead. And I think about self-care the exact same way.

I'm always prepared for a fucking disaster.

I care about prepping so much that, one time when I hosted a party, I made miniature earthquake bags as party favors to give out to friends to keep in the trunk of their cars. Because you never know when "the big one" is gonna hit, and what if my dear friend is stuck on a collapsing freeway with no water or first aid, having a panic attack during the apocalypse? Not happening. Cue the part on the show when they say, "And that's when I knew . . . I'm a prepper."

There are two major turning points in my life that made me into the Self-Care Prepper that I am today:

1. My struggle with severe depression
2. The discovery that I am an empath and highly sensitive person (HSP)

These two experiences totally transformed my life and shaped who I am now, and if there ever was a cheat code to the game of life I wanted to pass out to every creative boss bitch on the planet, it's how to handle both of these experiences. There are major hot zones in self-care that make it difficult for anyone to cope. Change. Transition. Loss/Grief. For me, I experienced all of the above without even knowing I was an empath/HSP, which meant everything hit even *harder*. Taking life's plot twists without understanding your own sensitivities as an empath or HSP is a real doozy. Especially if you're living an unconventional life as an artist.

I Get You Because I Am You

As an artist and songwriter, I am sensitive as fuck. For creatives, making art is so damn personal. We put our entire lives on the line for our art. We pour our freaking souls into it. The creative process alone is its own beast that we have to nurture, not to mention all the other crap that goes on in life. And here's the thing about empaths: We feel *everything*. (And we feel that shit deeply too.) We are **GIVERS**. We are overgivers. But oftentimes we overgive at the expense of ourselves. And that's where it stops being okay.

I'm here to make sure you are taking care of your MVP, which is **YOU**. Your endless sacrifices that leave you running on fumes serve no one. Being mentally, emotionally, physically drained and depleted is a complete disservice to yourself and everyone around you. There's no badge of honor in store for suffering as hard as you are. And I hate to break it to you, but there's also no one coming to rescue you from this problem except yourself. So let's find a way to keep your own cup full first, run safety checks on all your flights, so that you can continue to pour all that magical, loving, caring, creative genius energy onto the world.

Okay, so what makes me an expert? Why should you care what I have to say? Let's take a quick jump into my story so you know where I'm coming from.

My Story

I grew up half-Filipino in a very small town called Ladysmith, located on Vancouver Island, British Columbia. I started singing when I was five, songwriting as a teenager, and I made it my business to perform at every mall, church, talent show, and town event there was. At seventeen, I moved out on my own to Vancouver, BC, and started an internship at a recording studio where I could hone my craft of songwriting and learn how to produce my own music. I worked a bunch of shitty jobs as a waitress, a hostess, a grocery store clerk, a retail stock girl, whatever I could do to pay the rent. Then enters my first abusive relationship with a narcissistic alcoholic sex addict. (Fun, right?) This experience sent me on a downhill spiral into my first bout with severe depression at eighteen.

At my worst, I wanted to drown myself in my bathtub just to make it all stop. I'd quit my job. I'd stopped writing songs. I'd stopped doing things that once brought me joy. For months, I wasn't eating, I wasn't sleeping, and I was stuck in a total brain fog. I'd barely left my house or seen anyone. Everything felt difficult and pointless, and time became a blur. My whole life kind of blacks out at this point, and my lil' depressive moment lasted for about six months. These months were catastrophic for me. I pretty much crawled into my own hole and became suicidal, and I'd lost all motivation to do anything at all.

Eventually, by some miracle I began to reemerge but unfortunately continued riding that rollercoaster of a relationship for about another year. (I forgive you, younger self, for not knowing any better.) The relationship inevitably goes down in flames and rips my whole heart out. But this heartbreak would become one of my biggest blessings in disguise. Thankfully, I got away from that loser and began the process of rediscovering who I was.

At twenty-one, I hit a break! One of the songs I wrote about my loser ex-boyfriend took off on Canadian radio and hit number five on the Billboard Chart for Emerging Artists. Shortly after that, another one of my songs became the number one most-added song on Canadian radio, which sent me on a hot streak. I hit the road with my band and started touring over the country. For the next couple years, I performed at bars, radio stations, colleges, festival stages, showcasing at CMJ, Canadian Music Week, and North by Northeast (NXNE). During that time, my music started getting used in film and TV shows, I got to open up for a bunch of huge Canadian artists, people from all over the world started posting covers of my songs, and I got nominated for two Canadian Radio Music Awards. For someone who was severely depressed and wanted to die in a bathtub just a few years prior, this mental health recovery and career slay was pretty darn cool. It just goes to show that even when you're in the pits of hell, you never know what's waiting for you right around the corner.

After a couple years of touring Canada, I quickly realized I either had to be in New York or Los Angeles to immerse myself with some of the world's best songwriters and producers in order to land bigger opportunities for myself. So I did just that. At twenty-four, I saved up $20,000 in gig money and server tips, moved to New York City with two suitcases and a guitar, and never looked back. I lived in a tiny, expensive apartment in Bushwick with three other roommates and started writing and gigging all around the city. In New York, I met my husband (a music producer), where we spent five lovely years cowriting, collaborating, spending short chapters of our lives together in Harlem, Flatbush, and Bed-Stuy. In 2017, I decided I wanted to completely revamp my artist project and change my artist name to **DYLN**. Yep, I completely rebranded my entire identity and started from absolute scratch! (At twenty-eight!) Many people thought I was crazy for this, but I did it anyway.

Eventually, we moved to Los Angeles, got married, and started a whole new life together living the California dream. At thirty, I hit a low point in my relationships and found myself struggling emotionally in my therapist's office, only to have her tell me that **I am an empath/highly sensitive person (HSP).** This experience totally knocked my socks off and explained everything about me. *Everything.* In hindsight, it's truly embarrassing and frustrating how glaringly obvious it is to see why I struggled with being sensitive most of my life. Had I known even just a few coping mechanisms, things would've been a lot different. Learning I was an empath changed my life forever.

Some Highs and Lows

After two decades of working in the music industry as an artist, songwriter, and music producer, my work has appeared on
Billboard and been nominated for various music awards, including a Grammy. I've toured Canada and the US, played festivals,
and performed on award shows, TV, and radio. (And, I might
add, I've been self-managed for most of my career.) I've helped
dozens of artists and songwriters find their voice, to develop
a style and vision for themselves. But one of the most reward-
ing things I've ever done in my career is spend a couple years
touring high schools all over Canada, speaking to thousands of
students about the importance of mental health and how using
creativity is a powerful way to cultivate well-being.

The reason I toured in schools and talked about mental health
is simple: I really fucking care about this. The truth is, everyone
struggles. I've had the chance to see it firsthand, working with
some of the most talented, unique, inspiring, eccentric, creative
people. (Literal rock stars.) I've been in the room enough times to
see the common thread of challenges that creatives face. Everyone
hurts, and there's no shame in admitting that. I don't care what the
Internet says or what perfectly manicured lives people are portray-
ing online these days. *Everyone* struggles behind closed doors.

Because let's be real. There's absolutely no shortage of shitty
situations along the way. Being a risk-taker, it comes with the ter-
ritory. There's being broke and working lame-ass jobs for money.
There are disgusting, barfy situations with predatory men in the
industry (we all know how that goes). There are **BIG** rejections,
disappointments, and failures . . . And of course, there's sexism,
ageism, racism, homophobia, transphobia, self-limiting beliefs,
comparison traps, and doom-scrolling. There's feeling hopeless,
worthless, and wanting to quit. Over and over and over again.

Now, I am not a doctor. I am not a therapist. But I do have a PhD in independent artist kick-assery. That, I can most definitely help you with. So if you're looking for a self-care guide that speaks the language of an artist's life *and* sees the world through the lens of an empath, then I'm your girl! Because there's no one-size-fits-all strategy when it comes to self-care for an artist. Everyone copes in different ways and needs different things. That's why I'm here. There is a strategy that fits *YOU* perfectly. And I want to help you find it. I'm writing this book because **THIS IS THE BOOK I WISH I HAD AT THE START OF MY CAREER.** These are the little gems of knowledge that I wish I had known sooner. These are the things that would have made all the difference in the world to me when I was fourteen, eighteen, twenty-one, twenty-five, or even thirty! This book is a compilation of self-care tools that have helped me navigate a creative career as an empath and highly sensitive person. Yes, babe, I'm passing them to you!

Here's what you *don't* need: You don't need to be living in a state of complete overwhelm, absorbing the world's energies, unable to cope, shield, or protect yourself from overstimulating situations or environments. You don't need to be so burned out or so busy all the time that you can't recognize your own feelings. And you don't need to be in unsatisfying relationships where all you do is give and all they do is take. Basically, you don't need to be struggling this hard. So vow to yourself right now: "I am no longer available to deprioritize my own well-being as a **creative empath**."

What I really don't want for you is to be where I was when I was eighteen. Severely depressed in a bathtub, watching the water drip out the faucet, actually wanting to die. At my lowest point, I really didn't want to be here anymore. And that feeling of just wanting to invisibly slip away; it's *scary*. The brain can do some pretty wild shit when it's stuck on that depressive loop for too long. We don't want that for you. This is why we reach out for help. This is why we self-care.

If I can beat a prolonged bout of depression, ward off suicidal thoughts, and feelings of worthlessness and hopelessness, and still manage to blossom into a creative career AND find happiness AND find balance AND find passion/purpose/meaning in my life AND learn to thrive as an empath/HSP, then SO CAN YOU.

Let's Collab

As a professional songwriter, something I do with other artists and writers in the room is simply just be a soundboard for them. I listen. I listen to what they're going through, to what they're struggling with. They may be going through a breakup or getting trolled on the Internet, whatever it is. My job first and foremost is to listen to the artist and find out the message or story that they are trying to tell through their music. My role as a wingwoman-songwriter is to help them find their voice and vision, to facilitate what they're trying to say. Now, I want to do this exact same thing with YOU, except we're gonna collaborate on creating your self-care first-aid kit. So that you, my friend, can live your best life.

More than anything, I want to help you start by identifying your own needs. That way you can listen to your intuition and honor wherever you are in any given moment. As much as I love the idea of being prepared, you *can't* be prepared for everything. Shit happens. Life happens. And sometimes self-care has to be determined in the moment, like any unexpected disaster. When you suddenly find yourself drowning, you need to be able to know how to *give yourself a freakin' life raft!* Or, if necessary, build your own! I want to equip you with the best self-care strategies to keep your ass afloat so you can handle any emergency, get slaying with confidence, and make badass decisions every single day.

This way, when you're having a total meltdown, you'll have more than a finite set of solutions to individual problems—you'll have the ability to respond to any situation. You'll have a plan. And any time you're tempted to quit because you think your work is trash or you aren't good enough, talented enough, whatever enough, and you're considering throwing in the towel for good this time, I'll be the one to say, "Fuck that! Those are just your inner gremlins talking. You don't have to listen to a single word they're saying. In fact, they're fired immediately. Nobody's quitting anything." Let's wipe our tears, fix our crown, and call it a minor freak-out moment. Because the world *needs* you. And even when you're feeling like it's the apocalypse, I got you, boo.

Let me be your wingwoman, your cheerleader, your goddamn number one fan.

You got this.

CHAPTER ONE

Self-Care for Empaths and HSPs

The Unwoke Empath

I'm thirty years old, and all my relationships are falling apart. My two closest friends are bad for me. One is a total energy vampire, whose calls and texts I dread. The other is an absolute mess and can't ever seem to get her shit together. I have a habit of dishing out my energy to anyone who stands two feet in front of me. Whenever I get an earful of someone's problems, my little empath heartstrings get pulled on and my knee-jerk reaction is to listen, absorb, and offer uplifting words in hopes of fixing all their problems and taking away their pain (so I don't have to feel it). I'm quick to jump into the line of duty when it comes to everyone else's needs. Yet the awareness of my own needs is at zero. I'll spend an hour listening to someone talk about themselves and have that same person not return the simple courtesy of a "How about you? How're things with you?" I'm drained. I'm overwhelmed. I'm people-pleasing. My boundaries are shit. And I'm stressed the fuck out every single day.

This is where I hit empath rock bottom. I find it hard to unwind at the end of the day. I'm complaining ALL THE TIME to my husband. It suddenly occurs to me that all my fucks are being distributed to those around me and not a single one is being given in return. I'm angry. I'm sad. And I sort of crumble inside myself, realizing I put so much time, effort, and attention into relationships that give me nothing in return. I'll give and give and give, allowing others to take and take and take, yet I remain oblivious as to why I feel so depleted. Life as I know it turns into an emotional dumpster fire, and the light inside of me completely burns out.

This is how I ended up slouched in the corner of a couch, next to a box of tissues, in my therapist's office, thinking I needed self-care intervention.

"Have you heard of empaths or highly sensitive people?" She adjusted her glasses.

"No. What is that?"

"Well, they can be sensitive to certain sounds or smells, and they need more time to unwind because of all the energies they pick up and absorb throughout the day." As soon as she said, 'absorbing energies,' it was like somebody hit a gong. *Bonggg!* The clues were coming together.

"And it sounds unreasonable, but they can require up to two hours of alone time each day," she calmly, matter-of-factly stated the literal tea of an empath experience. Nobody had ever put into words what it had felt like to be me my entire life until that moment. She was describing exactly what it feels like to be an emotional sponge. Suddenly, *everything* clicked and made sense. This was why I'd been struggling all along. How on earth did I not know about this before? The day I discovered that I'm an empath and HSP was the day that changed everything for me. It felt like I'd been a zebra my whole life and never seen my own stripes until that very moment. Like holy fucking crap, I'm a zebra!

This realization was not only one of the biggest epiphanies of my life but also the *key* component I needed to know about myself in order to even approach my own self-care. My journey towards becoming a woke empath (an empath who's fully aware of one's own sensitivities) officially began. A fucking game changer, y'all.

What Are Empaths and Highly Sensitive People?

Dr. Judith Orloff, author of *The Empath's Survival Guide*, says being an empath and a highly sensitive person are not mutually exclusive. A person can be both. Many highly sensitive people are also empaths. Both empaths and HSPs typically have a strong desire to help others, find joy in nature, and require extra down-time to unwind from all the energies they absorb throughout the day. I like to think of Dr. Orloff as my empath mommy. The

27

OG badass doctor who's not only brought crucial information to the mainstream but has also held my hand through the discovery of what being an empath is all about.

The term Highly Sensitive Person (HSP) is still a relatively new phrase. Researched since the '90s, it was officially coined by Elaine and Arthur Arron in 1997. Generally speaking, an HSP has a lower threshold for stimulation and requires more time to process these inputs than most people. HSPs tend to have a sensitivity to light, loud sounds, certain smells, and may have an aversion to being in large groups or busy places. In other words, the nervous system of an HSP is more sensitive to stimuli. HSPs are hyperaware of their surroundings, enjoy quiet environments, need extra alone time to process experiences, and tend to be introverted.

Empaths take the experience of an HSP to a whole other level. They can sense subtle energies and pick up on nuances that most people miss (like having Spidey-senses). Empaths even have the ability to physically absorb another person's emotions into their own bodies and feel them as if they were their own. Weird, right? Because empaths can feel the emotions of people around them so intimately, they often struggle with separating their own emotions from those of others. (I can attest that this is one of the biggest downsides.) Like HSPs, empaths also require a lot of extra alone time to process events, experiences, social gatherings, but they can be introverted or extroverted.

Approximately 15-20 percent of the population (about one in five people) have the personality traits of an Empath/HSP. Creatives are often empaths and HSPs. However, this should not be misunderstood as a disorder, but rather a character trait. This trait is innate in the same way that you're born with a particular hair or eye color. There's even new evidence from a University of Cambridge study that shows how empathic we are is partly due to genetics.[1] I find it much easier to look at myself with kinder eyes knowing this. When you see others coping differently, you may feel like something is wrong with you, or wish you were "normal" like everyone else, but it actually means there's *nothing* wrong with you. Whether your empath gifts were environmentally induced or partly due to genetics, neither is your fault. It's not something you chose or caused. Having this perspective may prompt a little more self-compassion when empathing gets a little hard.

I remember going to a camp one summer. I was about thirteen. I'd never been to a summer camp before and, based on my friends' reviews, it was supposedly the shit. It's a week-long adventure with all your friends where you get to meet a whole bunch of new kids from all over the place. Although it was a Christian camp, none of us were Christians—we were just there for the fun. You and your besties are assigned a cabin, do all kinds of fun activities throughout the day, you praise Jesus for a minute, then basically just hang out, and make some awesome new friends. Sounds cool, right? Wrong.

To an empath/HSP child, being piled into a cabin full of six other hyper, rambunctious, squealing girls for seven days, with no exits and, yes, all sleeping next to each other, this is the equivalent of hell. By day three, I wanted to go home, and I think I actually did. I got a call for an acting audition, and I was thankful for the excuse to leave. Now, *parts* of this experience were fun—I did enjoy making arts and crafts—but I had no understanding on how to provide myself with the things I actually needed to feel sane. I had zero alone time, zero quiet time. I was constantly bombarded with stimulation from other kids,

---

[1] Warrier, Verun. "Study Finds That Genes Play a Role in Empathy," University of Cambridge, 12 Mar. 2018. https://www.cam.ac.uk/research/news/study-finds-that-genes-play-a-role-in-empathy.

activities, the zipline, Jesus. If I had *known* I needed more alone time for myself at that camp, I could have done so and enjoyed the entire experience more. Solitude and quiet time are like the gas stations for empaths. A single day of loaded social activity will leave us on E. If I had met my friend Awareness a little sooner, we would have been besties at first sight. Unfortunately, I wouldn't meet her until I was thirty.

Because the brain and nervous system of an empath/HSP processes information differently than the average person, it's crucial to understand the characteristics in order to properly create a self-care strategy. Without Awareness, many empaths and HSPs live completely overwhelmed and exhausted simply because they're uninformed of their own nature. (*Which was meeee for the longest time, hellooo!*)

Here are some of the character traits of empaths and highly sensitive people:

Character Traits of Empaths and HSPs	
Empath	**Highly Sensitive Person**
<ul><li>Deeply caring</li><li>Emotionally intelligent</li><li>Emotional sponge</li><li>Extremely observant and aware</li><li>Feels others' emotions intimately</li><li>Has trouble distinguishing someone else's emotions/ discomfort from their own</li></ul>	<ul><li>Easily overwhelmed by chaotic scenes</li><li>Has a strong sensitivity to light, sound, and smell</li><li>Has an aversion to large groups or busy places like malls, airports, busy restaurants</li><li>Highly sensitive and hyperaware of their surroundings</li></ul>

Character Traits of Empath and HSPs	
Empath	**Highly Sensitive Person**
• Highly sensitive to physical stimuli, like sights, sounds, etc. • Highly intuitive • May be introverted or extroverted • Likes nature and quiet environments • Needs a lot of alone time • Often called "sensitive" or accused of "overthinking" • Often feels drained, exhausted, or overwhelmed after social gatherings • Often has strong "gut feelings" or intuition about situations • Picks up on subtle cues or nuances • Requires extra downtime to unwind, decompress, and process information • Senses subtle energies • Upset by violence or cruelty of any kind • Thinks and feels more deeply than others	• Highly perceptive and may notice details others miss • Likes nature and quiet environments • Likes the comforts of home • Lower threshold for stimulation like social gatherings or loud concerts • Lower pain tolerance • Needs a lot of alone time • Needs extra time to process events and experiences • Often called "too sensitive" • Often intelligent, creative, empathic • Sensitive to scratchy or itchy clothing • Sensitive to violence or cruelty of any kind • Takes longer to wind down • Typically introverted

Character Traits of Creatives

- Ambitious
- Anxious
- Adaptable
- Curious
- Critical
- Courageous
- Disciplined
- Different/Unique
- Dreamers
- Determined
- Depressive
- Eccentric
- Emotional
- Empathetic
- Energetic
- Extroverted
- Focused
- Flexible
- Highly sensitive
- Highly intuitive
- Imaginative
- Independent
- Innovative
- Introverted
- Intelligent
- Moody
- Naive
- Open-minded
- Outside-the-box thinkers
- Overanalytical
- Passionate
- Problem-solvers
- Playful
- Reflective
- Risk-takers
- Rebellious
- Rule-breakers
- Self-absorbed
- Sensitive
- Trailblazers
- Visual

Drawing the connection between empaths, HSPs, and creatives (in my opinion) has been overlooked, misunderstood, and could possibly be the very crux of why creatives tend to struggle more mentally and emotionally in the first place. **Creativity requires sensitivity.** Empaths and HSPs feel everything on a much deeper level than others. Their sensitive nature and emotional intelligence makes them *excellent* creators and likely to be drawn to the arts. Art of any kind, whether it be music, visual arts, or film, involves channeling our own emotions and intellect to write a song, paint a picture, or make a film. This is why empaths and HSPs flourish in creative fields as they are the perfect conduits for them.

What if more creative people knew about this character trait or had more strategies available to them to cope with anxiety, depression, overwhelm, and exhaustion? Would the famous **27 Club** (a long list of famous artists who have died tragically at that age) even exist? What if more empaths and highly sensitive people took the time to really understand what is necessary to nurture these sensitivities?

The diagram below shows the many character traits that creatives, empaths, and HSPs can share. This is why self-care for creatives is abso-fucking-lutely non-negotiable.

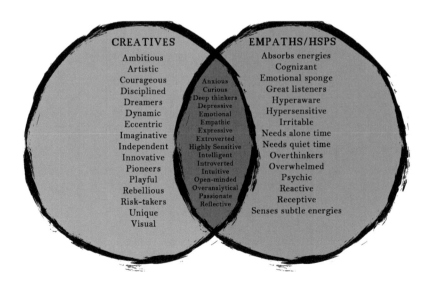

CREATIVES
Ambitious
Artistic
Courageous
Disciplined
Dreamers
Dynamic
Eccentric
Imaginative
Independent
Innovative
Pioneers
Playful
Rebellious
Risk-takers
Unique
Visual

Anxious
Curious
Deep thinkers
Depressive
Emotional
Empathic
Expressive
Extroverted
Highly Sensitive
Intelligent
Introverted
Intuitive
Open-minded
Overanalytical
Passionate
Reflective

EMPATHS/HSPS
Absorbs energies
Cognizant
Emotional sponge
Great listeners
Hyperaware
Hypersensitive
Irritable
Needs alone time
Needs quiet time
Overthinkers
Overwhelmed
Psychic
Reactive
Receptive
Senses subtle energies

Are you thinking that the Venn diagram above could just be one big circle? Samesies. Here it is as one giant bubble of the creative empath experience.

Creative Empaths/HSPs

Absorbs energies
Ambitious
Anxious
Artistic
Cognizant
Courageous
Curious
Deep thinkers
Depressive
Disciplined
Dreamers
Dynamic
Eccentric
Emotional
Emotional sponge
Empathic
Expressive
Extroverted
Great listeners
Highly sensitive
Hyperaware
Hypersensitive
Imaginative

Independent
Innovative
Intelligent
Introverted
Intuitive
Irritable
Needs alone time
Needs quiet time
Open-minded
Overanalytical
Overthinkers
Overwhelmed
Passionate
Playful
Pioneers
Psychic
Reactive
Rebellious
Receptive
Reflective
Risk-takers
Senses subtle energies
Unique
Visual

It's important to note that empaths and HSPs not only occupy the creative arts, but they often flock to careers in education and healthcare as teachers, counselors, doctors, physicians, nurses, and first responders. Empaths are *healers*. They may also lead very spiritual lives as energy healers, yoga instructors, reiki practitioners, astrologers, tarot readers, practitioners of witchcraft (like me), and so on! Being highly empathetic and sensitive are certainly not limited to one sector. And any and all professions have the potential to be creative. It's beyond beneficial for any empath/HSP to have a creative outlet, regardless of what field you work in. If crunching numbers or performing open heart surgery is part of your typical day-to-day life, perhaps adding a dimension of creativity in your life outside of work could be groundbreaking for you. The four types of empaths listed below make it pretty clear just how spiritual it can get.

The Four Types Of Empaths

- **Clairsentience**
  You sense the feelings and emotions of people, animals, places, and spirits.
- **Claircognizance**
  Information comes to you out of the blue and you believe it to be accurate and true.
- **Clairvoyance**
  You see images in your mind before they manifest.
- **Clairaudience**
  You hear messages inside your mind. Spirits may have conversations with you.

CLAIRSENTIENCE

- Sensitive to surroundings
- Easily senses the energy of a person or place
- May have physical or emotional reactions to large crowds
- You experience emotional changes when around other people
- You sense what people are feeling
- You empathize with people easily
- You may feel the presence of ghosts or spirits
- You can physically feel people's pain
- You experience others' emotions as if they are your own
- You say "I feel" phrases

CLAIRCOGNIZANCE

- You know when someone is telling the truth or not
- Your mind is active and always coming up with new ideas, especially with new projects
- You receive answers to things but don't know where they came from
- You have inspirational and creative ideas
- You say "I know" phrases

CLAIRAUDIENCE

- You typically listen more than you talk
- You communicate with plants and animals
- You often feel you are receiving telepathic information
- You may provide wise information or advice but not know where you got it from
- You say "I hear" phrases

CLAIRVOYANCE

- You have vivid dreams
- You may daydream a lot
- You are very imaginative
- When you close your eyes, you may see pictures, objects, shapes, or colors
- You may see flashes of light or movements in the corner of your eyes
- You say "I see" phrases

The Gift and Curse of Being an Empath/HSP

If you're thinking you may be an empath or HSP, there's a quiz at the end of this chapter that could help you gain some clarity. You may already be noticing in your life some of the challenges an empath might face. Empaths experience being human like a seven-layer dip. There's a lot going on in there. All the flavors get messy, but it's damn delicious. On the plus side, our sensitivities allow us to create incredible things with art, music, and film because of the depth with which we think and feel. We're able to give the gift of understanding, empathy, and encouragement to the world and those around us. (How awesome is that?) And our desire to help others makes us natural healers, leaders, and uplifters.

However, and this probably comes as no surprise, there are some unfortunate downsides. The needs of empaths/HSPs are often misunderstood by non-empath/HSP people, and they often get labeled as "too sensitive" or "difficult." These traits can feel like a burden, especially when non-empath/HSP people seem to be coping and handling things more easily, simply because they don't think or feel in the same way. I can't tell you how many times I've looked over at my husband in sheer envy at his ability to fall asleep instantly, while I lie awake, still mentally debriefing the entire day. Not that he doesn't have any empathy, he does. It's just that the day's experiences move through me mentally/emotionally in a *completely* different way. If he were an instant coffee cup that brews in five seconds, I am the giant coffee pot that takes ten minutes to brew coffee because there's so much more moving through my emotional filter.

Constantly absorbing energies makes it difficult to cope with daily living. Being an empath/HSP is not something you can just turn on or off. Our capacity for caring for others is higher, often at the expense of ourselves. Because we pick up so much information, we need to process it, release it, and be able to unwind from it. Overall, it takes us much longer to process all the emotional and physical stimuli that bombard us throughout the day. Too much of anything, even the good stuff, can be exhausting to an empath. Overstimulating events or environments may be a shock to our systems. If we're not careful about our boundaries, certain situations can easily derail us and knock us off our paths. As a rule of thumb, empaths/HSPs need to be able to return to an energetic baseline to avoid burnout or overwhelm.

If you identify as an empath or HSP, understand that you are *not* broken or damaged. Despite the difficulties you may encounter from everyday life, you have a unique talent that you should protect at all costs. Honoring your needs is an act of self-love and respect. Rather than seeing your gift as a burden, it's important to reframe your paradigm of these traits and start seeing them as superpowers! For example, I'm a *much* better citizen of the world when I can see through a lens of empathy. I'm a much better songwriter when I can pick up someone else's energy and put subtle details into the music. And I'm better able to hold a conversation or space for someone who may need help or may be struggling. Seeing the *good* in your gifts will help you to honor them and accept yourself for who you really are. With Awareness and practice, you can learn how to cope with sensitivity and avoid some of the major pitfalls. The proper tools and techniques will help you to stay grounded, take better care of yourself, and nurture your magical superpowers so that you can continue to make brilliant art and live your life from a position of empowerment!

Recovery for Empaths

It is essential for empaths and HSPs to recognize their own limits to overwhelming people, places, and situations, and to set healthy boundaries with energy drainers. Creating your own personal code of conduct for stressful circumstances, situations, or environments is a must. Having a plan and an idea of what gives you comfort when you're needing to recharge is super beneficial. Here are all of my favorite go-to comforts I like to do as an empath/HSP.

Alone Time

This is like the holy grail of self-care to an empath! The elixir that cures all. Empaths and HSPs need *plenty* of alone time to rest, reset, and recharge. We need our own space to feel comfortable, and we need quiet time to reflect, unwind, and decompress. It's actually recommended to have two hours of alone time a day. This adds up to about one day (of waking hours) per week and a whole week per month. Absurd, right? Because living with added sensitivity requires more time to process emotions, events, and experiences, alone time is absolutely critical for an empath.

The Recommended Amount of Alone Time for an Empath/HSP:

- Approximately two hours per day
- One day (of waking hours) per week
- Approximately one week per month

This can seem like a totally unrealistic benchmark, and perhaps you're simply unable to meet this requirement at the moment, *BUT* at the very least, this should give you an idea of *just how important* alone time is to an empath/HSP. Prioritizing this single factor alone will have a massive impact on your health and well-being as an empath/HSP. Think of some ways you can begin incorporating more alone time into your days, or begin scheduling chunks of alone time into your calendar.

How to Make More Alone Time

- Schedule thirty minutes of alone time in your calendar two to three times per week.

- Plan a fun date for yourself once a month where you take yourself out.
- Incorporate twenty minutes of mindfulness meditation in your morning routine.
- Journal for thirty minutes at the end of the day.
- Schedule time weekly to write, reflect, journal.
- Take a fifteen minute walk alone on your lunch break.
- Plan a long, leisurely nature hike or walk.
- Meditate for five minutes in silence before you start your work day.
- If you normally sleep with your partner, try to find a way to sleep alone sometimes.
- Take a nice long bath once or twice a week.
- Create a solo morning workout routine.

Grounding

Grounding is a way to get centered and present within your own body, to bring yourself and your state of awareness to the present moment. Grounding can be as simple as closing your eyes and taking a few deep breaths to get connected to your body. It could be drawing your attention to five things in your surroundings and noticing sights, sounds, smells, and sensations. It also can mean lying on the ground. It can be on your floor, on the grass, or literally on the bare earth. Feeling the earth support your body can be incredibly comforting and inspire a state of surrender and calm. You can also get grounded by forest bathing or taking a nature walk.

Cocooning

Cocooning is kind of exactly what it sounds like. Think of a butterfly in its cocoon before it flutters away into the world. Empaths/ HSPs can benefit a lot from cocooning themselves before or after highly social events or intense workload days. Absorbing intense energies means having to reclaim your own physical body and differentiate it from the outside world. The idea is to enclose yourself in a cocoon and give yourself time to regenerate.

Try wrapping yourself in a nice big blanket or wearing a big comfy hoodie or sweatpants that can create a comfort barrier between your physical body and the outside world. There's no set time limit or wrong way of doing it—just do what feels most comforting to you. You may need to cocoon for an entire evening before a very big day at work or after a social gathering, or you may need to spend a full day or two cocooning before or after a big travel trip.

Bath Time

Water is, of course, physically cleansing, but it can also help to wash away all the daily stressors, tensions, emotions, and thoughts of the day. Water is incredibly healing and comforting to empaths. Put some Epsom salts in the bath to relax muscle tension, body aches, and pains to help prepare you for a great night's sleep. Make bath time an extra enchanting, restorative process for you by putting a little magic into it.

Experimenting with essential oils, bath salts, and even herbs like lavender, rose, or chamomile can be a nice touch for your bath experience. You don't have to spend eternity, and it doesn't have to break the bank either! You can simply light some candles next to some crystals on the edge of the tub and drop some rose petals on top of the bath suds. Whatever makes bath time a little more soothing and luxurious for you, *do it!* Putting in a little extra effort into loving on yourself is totally worth the restorative experience.

Unstructured Time

Empaths and HSPs can benefit massively by including unstructured time in their calendars. There are a couple trigger points for empaths and HSPs, and rushing is one of them. Having too many meetings back to back without breaks and having a rigid work schedule can be a recipe for disaster. Building in some unstructured time can feel like a breath of fresh air to an empath. While others may see it as wasteful or unproductive, that empty space on your calendar can be a much-needed relief. So put it on there! It feels *really* nice to occasionally relieve any pressures to be anywhere or do anything by a certain time. Allowing this leeway in between commitments, engagements, and functions allows for a smoother transition, a shift in energies, and a moment to regain composure. When you get to that unstructured time, you can use it to do whatever you might need in that moment. It can be used to be productive in a less constrained way, or it can be used for a nap or leisure time.

Empath Problems

Because empaths can often internalize another person's emotions as if they are their own, it can become difficult to differentiate between what someone else may be feeling and what they (the empaths) may be feeling personally. During social gatherings, it's often helpful to ask yourself if a feeling or symptom is actually yours. It's possible you could be absorbing some heartbreak listening to your bestie talk about her recent breakup. It's possible you could be feeling someone else's nervous energy when they're feeling awkward at a networking event. It's possible you could be inheriting feelings of self-consciousness or stress from someone who is having self-esteem issues. I like to think of this mix of emotions like clothes spinning around in the wash. Empaths have problems sorting through their emotional laundry. Sometimes what's in their laundry bin isn't theirs. When you sort your laundry, you have to be able to say, "This is mine" and "This is not mine." Here's a technique I created that will help you quickly and easily sort through your emotions and figure out what's yours and what's not.

Technique: Emotion Separation

After a particularly stimulating evening out with friends, for example, write down on a piece of paper a list of all the things or emotions you felt that night. Sorta like dumping the laundry bin of clothes on the floor, write 'em all down so you can see them. Then, I want you to start sorting the laundry and claim what's yours and what isn't, labeling each feeling as "Mine" or "Not Mine" (or the name of the person you believe this feeling belongs to). Finally, you're going to claim what's yours and release what isn't. **Emotion separation is the act of separating or differentiating your feelings from the feelings of another person.** Here's how to to do it in three easy steps:

1. Write down your feels.
2. Label it. (Mine or Not Mine)
3. Claim it.

The example below shows you how you can quickly filter through your experience and dissolve any unwanted feelings you may be experiencing on behalf of others.

Emotions I Felt Tonight	
I felt excited and nervous to see my friends tonight.	Mine
I felt extremely hungry before dinner.	Mine
I felt self-conscious about my body when ordering dessert.	Julie
I felt awkward at the dinner table discussing politics.	Mine
I felt sad because of a recent job loss and change of career path.	James
I felt jealous or envious of people having a job they love.	James
I felt happy to spend a night out socializing.	Mine
I felt impatient waiting for the bill.	James
I felt the need to keep the conversation going.	Mine
I felt uncomfortable discussing my dating life.	Julie

In as little as five minutes, you can write down your feelings and label them, giving you full clarity on your emotions. As empaths, we can feel the full range of emotions of everyone around us and carry that with us when we arrive back home. Having a simple exercise like this can help you quickly identify which emotions are yours and which are not so you can easily release them and lovingly send them back to where they came from, giving you the permission to no longer wear or hold that emotion in your body.

The Mind, Body, Soul Technique

The mind, body, soul technique is a five minute check-in that allows you to see what you're feeling or experiencing. It's exactly what it sounds like. Write a line or two of what you're feeling in that particular moment in your mind, body, and soul. Are you feeling mentally scattered? Tension in your neck and shoulders? Or perhaps longing for some friend time? When you're having a hectic day, this five-minute exercise can ground you and allow you to bear witness to your own experience. This technique also helps empaths to see what their personal experience is without being clumped in with another person's.

Mind: My mind is feeling/experiencing:

_____
_____
_____
_____
_____
_____

Body: My body is feeling/experiencing:

_____

_____

_____

_____

_____

_____

Soul: My soul is feeling/experiencing:

_____

_____

_____

_____

_____

If you aren't in a position to write it down, this exercise can be done with your eyes closed and done as a meditation, anytime, anywhere.

Emotional Hangovers

Emotional Hangovers. Yes, they're a thing. I'll give you a perfect example. I had a pretty decent-sized fight with my husband one night. I was super emotional, and I remember smashing one of our pictures on the floor in a hot rage. Hey, these things happen. My emotions ran so high that my entire nervous system totally peaked, and I stayed up crying half the night. The next day, my husband was able to get up and go to work like everything was cool. I, on the other hand, needed an entire day just to emotionally and physically recover from a scene like that. This is true for me even when it's not an argument with my husband. It could be a tough conversation I had with a family member that left me distraught, or it could be a major disappointment at work. Whatever it is, empaths experience emotional hangovers. Our nervous systems can jump into overload from processing stimuli in a freeze, fight, or flight situation, leaving us, well, *shook*. We need extra time to recover from bigger emotions, likely because we tend to swim around in them a little bit longer.

Unwinding

Unwinding to an empath/HSP can be a hilarious and frustrating experience, especially next to someone who has not a single issue in being able to do so. Let's take my husband, for example. The man can put his head to his pillow and be asleep in 2.5 seconds. The amount of rage and jealousy I have toward this capability is high. I won't lie. Unwinding on an average day for me usually requires no phones, screens, TVs, or computers at least an hour before bed, some time to journal my thoughts and reflect on the day, do my skincare, get in my snuggies, put on some tea, and maybe read a book for a while until I get sleepy. On tough days, where something major has occurred, or if I've had a really full work day loaded with social activity, I immediately add an extra hour to my downtime. I may need to journal for longer to process my emotions, or I may need to take a bath to relax and let the day's energies just wash off my body. These are the kinds of things I **need** in order to feel even remotely sane. My husband, on other hand, whether he's had a tough day or not, can binge-watch an entire murder documentary (with full blood, guts, and gore) until midnight and still somehow make it to his pillow and be dead-ass asleep by 12:01 a.m.

High Absorbing Events

Parties

Here's a good one. Parties. Over the years I've hosted a bunch of them. I love getting everyone together, preparing the food, the booze, the decor, the spreads, all of it. Love a fucking party. So what happens is, before anyone comes over, I get hit with a wave of anxiety because I realize I'm about to absorb a bunch of energy that isn't mine. We'll spend the whole night drinking and talking to our friends. Get a little tipsy, have some laughs, then everyone goes home.

The next morning it looks like a bomb went off in our house. Empty bottles and cups everywhere, half-eaten charcuterie boards on the counter. Glitter is also everywhere. Half-drunk me gets a Starbucks sandwich and a coffee to stabilize. Then I spend the next couple hours processing every single interaction I had with everyone the night before. I'll literally replay conversations, trying to make sense of them. I'll say things to my husband like, "Do you think Rachelle is happy in her relationship? I sensed she's a little unhappy," or "I feel like Julie is struggling with money," or "I think James really wants to start his own business, but he's afraid of taking the risk." Whatever my little Spidey senses picked up, I'll talk through them. It seems like I'm analyzing things to death, and I am. But this is what my process of sifting through my emotional laundry (what's mine, what isn't) can look like before I can move on with my day.

Funerals

Here's another good one. Funerals. While a funeral is a tough experience for anyone who is attending and experiencing a loss, an empath is going to feel *everyone's* feelings at that event. This was particularly true for me when my uncle passed away. I knew my uncle, but we weren't particularly close. Still, he used to come over to our house *all the time* to play cards with my dad. When he died, I saw my father cry probably for the first time in my life. After his funeral, I felt incredibly sad, thinking of his kids, his wife, my dad, everyone who loved him so much. I felt what they were feeling. This is a perfect example of feeling deep sadness and loss, even though it isn't exactly yours. The difference between people who have empathy and being an empath is simply that empaths wear the emotions as if they are their own. Empaths experience the event as if it's their own experience. What I was feeling wasn't necessarily the loss of my close relationship with my uncle, but the loss that everyone else who loved him at that funeral was feeling.

Setting Boundaries as an Empath

Setting boundaries in general can be difficult. Add being an empath to the equation and it's even harder. Because your natural instinct is to want to help everyone, you may end up spreading your energetic resources thin. But it's now your job as a newly empowered empath to get super-duper great at identifying and setting your boundaries like a boss. Let's look at the types of boundaries and reflect on what some of your boundaries are, plus effective ways of communicating them to others!

Types Of Boundaries	
PHYSICAL	This refers to whenever and however you are being touched, and by whom. Examples: Not wanting to be hugged by a stranger or touched by a yoga instructor.
EMOTIONAL	This refers to something that hurts your feelings (e.g. a nasty comment) or deciding when to share or not to share personal information. For example, not feeling comfortable sharing personal things about your life to someone new.
INTELLECTUAL	This refers to your personal thoughts, opinions, and beliefs. An intellectual boundary is crossed when someone dismisses or belittles your ideas, thoughts, or beliefs.
VERBAL	This refers to the way in which someone speaks to you. Verbal boundaries can be crossed with rude, passive-aggressive, or hurtful comments.
SEXUAL	This refers to how people treat you in sexual situations. A sexual boundary is crossed when someone touches you in a way that makes you uncomfortable or when they want you to do something sexually that you don't want to do.

Types Of Boundaries	
TIME	This refers to how you decide to use your time. A time boundary is violated when someone takes up or demands too much of your time. A time boundary can look like only spending *x* amount of time on a task or not working on the weekends.
MATERIAL	This refers to material items. An example could be not wanting to lend out all your clothes to that one friend who keeps asking (who never returns them, btw).

Communicating Your Boundaries

Communicating your boundaries is vital for keeping yourself in a safe space and for allowing others the chance to better understand you in terms of what's okay and what's not okay. Setting boundaries is an act of self-love and self-respect, and anyone who truly loves, supports, and cares for you will absolutely honor and respect your boundaries. Communicating healthy boundaries can sound like:

"I'd really love to be able to make it out tonight, but I've been feeling a little overworked lately, and I really need to catch up on rest."

"When you made that comment earlier about my body, it really hurt my feelings. I'd really appreciate it if you'd no longer make any comments about my body."

"I'm not really up for discussing that right now."

"I'd really appreciate not being touched today in class. I'll respond better with verbal adjustments. Thank you."

"Hey, I know you didn't mean any harm by this, but it reminded me of a boundary that I have that I'd love to tell you about."

If you're new to setting boundaries for yourself, it may feel a little awkward at first, but the friends and family who love and care about you the most will likely respond positively. This communication will actually end up deepening your relationship, strengthening your connection, and building your self-confidence in your ability to ask for what you need unapologetically. Because let's remind ourselves that setting boundaries is *important* and never warrants an apology.

Now, sometimes the people we love and who love us end up crossing our boundaries even when we've clearly set them. Sometimes, it's unintentional and quickly remedied, but when a loved one seems to keep violating your boundaries and causing you harm or an inconvenience, it's time to consider a few things: (a) How long will you continue to accept this person treating you in this manner? (b) What needs to change about the situation to make it better for you? We can communicate our boundaries all we want, but we don't get to control how people treat us. Fortunately, we always get to decide how we respond. There are a couple ways to respond differently when someone keeps pushing our buttons.

Communicate a Consequence

Let's say you're a very punctual person, and one of your boundaries is needing to be on time because if you aren't it makes you an anxious mess and totally ruins your entire day. And let's say you have one friend who's *always* fucking late and hanging out with her means that when you go to pick her ass up, she has you sitting in the driveway waiting for fifteen minutes, long enough to jumpstart your anxiety. Meanwhile, she's finishing her make-up, not seeming to care at all. (Even when you've told her the way you feel about time.) This is where communicating a consequence could be useful.

"Listen, I know we previously discussed how being late really bothers me, and it seems like since we spoke about that I've still been showing up late to things. In the future, if this continues, it's best for me not to go with you to things where being punctual matters to me."

Something like this allows for a second round of communication before choosing a different course of action. If this person's behavior remains exactly the same, you absolutely can and should change the way you engage or interact with this person.

Consider Distance or Disengaging

Too much boundary crossing could mean putting some distance between you and the people who keep doing it. You can decline invitations to places, not participate in unproductive conversations, and disengage or walk away entirely from disrespectful behavior. You can let them know why you're disengaging (if you want), or you can just decide to put some more space between you to protect yourself from any harm they may be causing you. You get to be in charge of how you adjust to someone else's poor behavior and to consider what feels best for you.

Dealing with a Narcissist

I grew up with a narc. Then I later dated one, and it wasn't until much later in life that I experienced a spiritual aha moment and recognized the similarities of both of these figures in my life. Empaths have a tendency to attract narcissists. It's a thing. Empaths have a giving, nurturing nature, and a narc's main goal is to find narcissistic supply (i.e., excessive attention and admiration) to affirm their impaired self-esteem. Narcissists fear they're undesirable, so they crave constant adoration and praise. It helps them avoid facing their own deep shame, unworthiness, and unhealed trauma. Empaths, sadly, are an easy target.

While the exact cause of narcissistic personality disorder is unknown, some researchers think neglectful or overprotective parenting may increase a child's chances of developing the disorder. In psychological literature, personality disorders are thought to be caused by a combination of genetic and environmental influences.

Experts say that up to 5 percent of the population have narcissistic personality disorder (NPD). The trouble with determining how common NPD actually is arises from the fact that those people would first have to seek treatment in order to be diagnosed. Generally speaking, people with NPD don't think (or want to think) anything is wrong with them, so they rarely seek help.

In my case, I experienced trauma with a narc growing up, and it makes sense that I'd later attract one as a boyfriend later on in life. (People love what's familiar, even if it is abusive.) It's this exact shitstorm of dealing with narc abuse that catapulted me into finding my spiritual journey with witchcraft in the first place. Your girl needed some *serious* healing. But I'll get into that later . . .

It's important to note that narcissism exists on a spectrum, and people can absolutely exhibit certain tendencies and behaviors without being considered a full-blown narcissist. For clarity, in this section, I'm referring to full-blown narcissists and their particular brand of abuse that often severely impacts empaths.

Common Narcissist Characteristics and Behaviors

- Abusive (mentally, emotionally, physically, or financially)
- Appears charming

- Arrogant
- Belief that they are smarter than everyone else
- Chronic envy and jealousy
- Competitive
- Deep insecurity
- Exaggerates their talents or achievements
- Excessive need for attention
- Expects special treatment
- Grandiose sense of self
- Highly intelligent
- Highly manipulative
- Inflated ego
- Insistent that nothing is ever their fault
- Intolerant of being less than perfect
- Lacks empathy
- Need for constant praise or admiration
- Preoccupation with illusions of power, success, or beauty
- Reacts negatively or or explosively to criticism
- Reacts defensively or changes the subject to avoid criticism
- Refuses to or is unable take responsibility for their actions or words
- Refuses to acknowledge or respect others' boundaries
- Represses insecurities
- Tendency to give unsolicited advice
- Tendency to hijack conversations to make themselves feel better or superior
- Tendency to take advantage of others
- Tendency to hold grudges
- Unable or unwilling to recognize the needs of others
- **Love bombing** - Showering someone with affection/attention in order to influence or manipulate them later
- **Crazy making** - Causing someone to question their own

reality through gaslighting and passive-aggressive, dismissive behavior

- **Hoovering** - Using emotional manipulation to lure someone back into a toxic or abusive relationship
- **Triangulating** - Emotionally abusing by bringing in a third party or person to further manipulate and control someone by creating conflicts or causing further doubt

Being able to determine the difference between a person who has narcissistic tendencies and a full-blown narcissist can be difficult. This is why narc abuse is such a bitch. Outsiders may not see the signs of this harmful human being at all; in fact, they may think he is a "good person" and simply miss (or unconsciously ignore) the red flags of his behavior entirely. The other thing that makes narcs dangerous is they are often very charismatic, appear highly intelligent, and they have the ability to perform manufactured empathy (when it serves them) so they can appear as the hero or "good guy" whenever convenient for them.

Empaths experiencing narcissistic abuse can often feel like they are walking on eggshells, be confused about their emotions, blame themselves for everything, dissociate from reality, become fearful of speaking up, and tolerate emotional, mental, and/or even physical abuse. Empaths may even have a hard time believing that their own abuse is real. (This was true for me.) One of the wonderful things about narc mind-fuckery is that it makes you question your reality, second-guess your decisions, and wonder "Is it my fault? Am I a bad person? Am I the narc?" (That's the effect of abuse and gaslighting talking.) The thing is, narcs don't even ask themselves those kinds of questions. So no, if you're sitting there questioning whether or not you are a narcissist, you are not a narcissist.

Here's the thing. What makes dealing with a full-blown narcissist so effing difficult is the holding on to hope that they're ever going to change. They won't. There may be a miniscule number (like 0.00000001 percent) of narcissists on the planet who have somehow miraculously gained some self-awareness AND the willpower to actually put in the work to recognize their toxic, abusive behavior and genuinely want to work in it. But the reality of Narc-land is that most of the time, they simply don't change. Ever. That's why narcissistic abuse can go on for years. Every word, every action, every thought, every move, every motivation, every aim is solely to serve themselves and fuel their narcissistic supply.

Cutting Ties with a Narc

Narc abuse can get nasty. And dangerous. If you find yourself in one of these situations, cutting ties with a narc is likely your only option. Reach out to trusted friends and family for support, join a narc abuse support group, speak with a therapist, and know there are all kinds of resources and numbers to call available to you **at the end of this book.** Your decision to cut ties with a harmful person (no matter who it is) is absolutely valid, real, and necessary to preserve your mental and emotional well-being. Moving *forward* with your life and concentrating on your healing is the most important thing. Here are two strategies, in my experience, that have been the most effective tools in dealing with narcissists.

Going No Contact

If possible, by far the best method is to cut all contact with this person. The effects of narc abuse want you to remain like a moth to a flame. It's tempting to be around, but we all know that whenever you play with fire, you're going to get burned. Oftentimes, we want to keep touching the flame because of the illusion that it *could be* something more pleasant, like warmth. But fire is fire, honey, and if you keep throwing yourself in it, you're gonna be *toast!* Block phone numbers and social media accounts. Remove this person from your life entirely and cut *all* access they have to you. Continue to support yourself through therapy, support groups and/or with the help of friends or family.

Grey Rock Method

If for some reason you have to remain in contact with a narc, try the Grey rock method. Narcs want to trigger an emotional reaction in you so they can use it against you later. Don't give them the satisfaction by refusing to react at all. Give short, straightforward answers and hide any emotions whatsoever. Make all interactions with this person as uninteresting and unrewarding as possible. The name of this method literally means to be as boring and unemotional as a grey rock.

Learning to Embrace Your Needs as an Empath/HSP

By now, you've probably grasped that empaths and HSPs simply need a different set of self-care skills than most people. In the beginning, as an unaware empath, you may find yourself thinking something is wrong with you because you can't cope with things or operate the way others do. But once you become aware of your tendencies and reactions to the onslaught of daily stimuli, your needs as an empath/HSP will start to click.

If you go to buy a plant, the first thing you do is find out what type of plant it is and the exact conditions it needs to thrive. Full sun, part sun? How much water a week? Being an empath or HSP is no different. You will thrive under certain conditions, so give yourself the opportunity of understanding what they are. Learn how to give yourself the best chances of not withering away, and let yourself bloom and bask in the sunlight! Embracing your nature as an empath is a powerful form of self-love and self-acceptance. Make a note of the key things you'll need to prioritize as an empath/HSP in order to remain empowered, not drained by your traits.

A TOOLBOX FOR
EMPATHS AND HSPS

Get plenty of alone time.

Allow time to reflect and process events.

Do some grounding.

Try cocooning.

Use bath time for unwinding.

Add unstructured time in your calendar.

Use the Emotion Separation technique.

Try the Mind, Body, Soul technique.

Create boundaries with overwhelming people, places, situations.

Remove "energy vampires" and toxic people.

Learn the signs of a narcissist.

Go no contact.

Use the Grey rock method.

Self-Care for Empaths and HSPs Workbook

Quiz: Are You an Empath or HSP?

Take this quiz to help you identify whether you might be an empath or highly sensitive person.

Are You an Empath or HSP?	
I care so much about others that I often neglect my own needs.	Yes/No
I have been labeled as "too sensitive," shy, or introverted.	Yes/No
I frequently get overwhelmed or anxious.	Yes/No
I get overwhelmed in large crowds or gatherings.	Yes/No
I am sensitive to light, smells, sounds.	Yes/No
It takes me longer to wind down at the end of the day.	Yes/No
Making decisions can sometimes take longer.	Yes/No
I often feel frazzled in chaotic places or scenes.	Yes/No

Are You an Empath or HSP?	
I typically feel or think more deeply than those around me.	Yes/No
I am hyperaware of my surroundings.	Yes/No
I am acutely aware of nonverbal cues like facial expressions, body language.	Yes/No
I know when someone is lying, cheating, manipulating, or has an agenda.	Yes/No
I have a strong intuition.	Yes/No
When someone is in pain, I feel that pain intimately.	Yes/No
Arguments and yelling make me feel physically unwell.	Yes/No
I need a lot of alone time to rest and recover.	Yes/No
I feel people's feelings as if they are my own.	Yes/No
I tend to get overwhelmed, exhausted, or drained after social situations.	Yes/No
I am overwhelmed by loud noise, strong odors, or bright lights.	Yes/No
I sometimes feel like I don't fit in or respond to things like others do.	Yes/No
Scratchy clothes bother me.	Yes/No
I overeat to cope with stress or emotions.	Yes/No
I am overwhelmed by multitasking.	Yes/No

Are You an Empath or HSP?	
I feel replenished in nature.	Yes/No
I have a low threshold for pain.	Yes/No
I have strong reactions to medications or caffeine.	Yes/No

If you answered "yes" to a majority of these questions, you are likely an empath or HSP.

What Are Your Comforts?

Take a moment to reflect on what gives you comfort. What gives your mind, body, and soul the feeling of relaxation, restoration, or safety? Write down your favorite comforts.

_____

_____

_____

_____

_____

_____

_____

_____

_____

_____

_____

_____

Here are some of mine:

- Taking a long bubble bath with candles, Epsom salts, and crystals
- Writing in a journal to reflect on my thoughts, feelings, and emotions
- Having a cup of tea and reading a good book
- Writing out my goals and desires
- Taking a nice long afternoon nap
- Curling up on the couch with my favorite childhood movie
- Cooking a delicious meal for myself
- Taking a walk outside and savoring the sun, sky, and plants
- Indulging in a longer skin or hair care routine
- Watching a TED talk or a Masterclass
- Browsing the aisles at a bookstore
- Shopping at metaphysical stores for crystals, trinkets, or spell supplies

What Does Alone Time Look Like to You?

Alone time is absolutely non-negotiable for empaths and HSPs. If you've identified as an empath or HSP, how would you prefer to spend your alone time? Do you like to read in a quiet room? Spend time journaling in the morning? Go window shopping or to a museum by yourself? Or perhaps cuddle up with your favorite show?

Write out some of your favorite ways to spend alone time.

_____

_____

_____

_____

_____
_____

How can you schedule in or create more alone time in your day? Your week? Your month?

_____
_____
_____
_____
_____
_____

Identify Energy Drainers

Write out all of the things that zap your energy, kill your mood/vibe, weigh you down and make you feel low-vibing frequencies. It can be people, places, environments, or situations. Anything that drains your energy and dims your spirits. Make a note of which drainers you can start limiting, avoiding, or eliminating completely.

_____
_____
_____
_____
_____
_____
_____
_____
_____
_____

_____

_____

Identify Energy Raisers

Write out a few things that raise your energies back up again after you've been drained by people, places, or situations. Sometimes, we have to participate in things that drain our energy levels, and it's important to have a plan to immediately replenish them. What activities or things help to raise your energy back up again?

_____

_____

_____

_____

_____

_____

_____

_____

_____

_____

Boundaries

What boundaries do you have with certain people, places, or environments, or with your physical body or your mental space? Write down anything that comes to mind that you find to be off-limits for the sake of your own well-being. Some examples could be: I can only spend *x* amount of time around this one person I find to be triggering, or I have to drive myself to the party so that I can have the ability to leave when I've had enough social activity. Write down any physical, mental, emotional, sexual, material, or situational boundaries you may have. Do you absolutely hate being hugged by strangers? Despise talking about politics at the dinner table? Don't want to talk about your dating life at the next family gathering?

_____

_____

_____

_____

_____

_____

_____

_____

_____

_____

_____

_____

CHAPTER TWO

Mindset, Basics and Routines

Mindset

My dad used to say, "You have to work really hard for what you want." To this day, I don't disagree. But the tone of his voice, bone dry and so matter-of-fact, made it seem like if you weren't working yourself really hard every day, then you weren't worth shit. It's a thin line between teaching work ethic and tying your self-worth to that work ethic.

Dad grew up on a farm in rural Saskatchewan as one of thirteen kids. His job was to work, provide, look after the land, care for his siblings, and do whatever he had to do to survive. One year, all he and his family ate for an entire year was eggs because that's all they had. The circumstances of his childhood, while obviously very different from mine and my siblings' (microwave pizzas and video games included), laid the groundwork for his mindset toward "self-care." Nobody knew that luxury. To him, if you were bumming around, you were worthless and didn't stand a chance at survival. He used to pop his head into the living room to catch a glimpse of us eating ice cream and playing Mario Kart. He'd scoff and say, "Life of Riley!"—an old-timey phrase used to describe an easy and carefree life. And I used to think, "Who the fuck is Riley?"

As time went on and we were being raised by workaholic Iron Man, I started to shape my own beliefs around work ethic as the holy grail of "being good, worthy, and lovable." Self-care was as nonexistent as the words my father would use to describe his own emotions. (Crickets.) I say all this to point out where I got some of my mindset toward self-care. How I would internalize taking a nap or taking a break as lazy, bad, or wrong. Why I'd tell myself that if my fingers weren't bleeding from playing guitar then I just wasn't working hard enough. And if I wasn't working hard enough, I couldn't be loveable. Therefore, my mindset became "*Self-care is for wimps!*"

I continued to pick up a few stinky beliefs about self-care in all kinds of places. The music industry pats people on the back for doing three writing sessions a day, attending networking events every night, and churning out records nonstop. Our culture historically congratulates those who self-sacrifice, work tirelessly, survive multiple mental breakdowns, and still somehow come up with a Grammy. That's the type of shit that gets praised. Our society is not giving you a standing ovation for taking a nap.

The great thing about our beliefs is that we get to rewrite them. We get to say, "Hey! I don't actually believe in this and I believe in this instead!" Mindsets and beliefs get picked up no matter where you turn, but it's ultimately up to you to decide what you want to believe. Now, I believe in working really hard *AND* embracing self-care. Yes, they can coexist. No one is painting the Sistine Chapel if they haven't eaten or slept in days. It's just not happening.

Technique: Rewrite the Belief

Let's take a peek at your mindset towards self-care and identify any potentially self-limiting beliefs that may be stopping you from prioritizing it. Unhelpful beliefs can sound like "Self-care is for lazy people" or "Massages are a waste of money." Whatever it is, let's uncover any mindsets or beliefs that are currently holding you back from engaging in your own self-care.

Here's how to **Rewrite the Belief** in four easy steps.

1. Write the belief.
2. Identify where it's coming from.
3. Give it a rating.
4. Rewrite the belief.

Let's try using your current beliefs around self-care as an example.

What are your current self-limiting thoughts, feelings, beliefs around self-care? It could look like what mine used to: "Self-care makes you a wuss. Who the hell has time? Taking a nap makes you lazy AF." Whatever it is. Write it down.

_____

_____

_____

_____

_____

_____

Where is it coming from? When you first think or hear this thought, feeling, or belief, where is it coming from? Whose voice do you hear in your head? Your mom, dad, sister, brother, friends, coworkers, society?

Now for the fun part. Do you actually believe it?
Give it a Yes, No, or Maybe. Rate it on a scale from one to ten how much you actually believe it. (One being "Not at all" and ten being "I fully subscribe to this belief.")

Then, rewrite the belief. Take each of your thoughts/beliefs

73

about self-care and rewrite them one by one. Write out the exact opposite of each statement or what you actually WANT to believe.

_____

_____

_____

_____

_____

Let's use my old belief system as an example:

Old Belief vs. New Belief

"Self-care is for wimps."	"Self-care is for boss bitches."
"Naps make you lazy."	"Naps are the bomb and help me to kick ass."
"I can't afford a monthly massage."	"Massages are key to my well-being."

Finally,

WRITE YOURSELF A SELF-CARE MANTRA

Let's take a few of these awesome new beliefs you now subscribe to and make one giant, epic mantra that encompasses the permission you easily give to yourself so that your self-care is priority numero uno at the drop of a dime no matter what. Here are some that feel good to me.

Self-care is my secret sauce to success.

Self-care is the smarter and more enjoyable way towards my goals.

The better I take care of myself, the better I can take care of others.

WRITE YOURS

_____

_____

_____

_____

_____

Great, now say it out loud right now. Post it somewhere where you can see it every day. Anytime you experience resistance towards allowing yourself to self-care, you get to say this mantra loud and proud. Lovely! Now that we have self-limiting beliefs towards self-care out of the way, let's continue on to thriving, shall we?

Sometimes, Self-Care Is a Basic B*tch

A few years back, I was sitting in my therapist's office asking her for some self-care tips. I was prepared for her to totally psychoanalyze me and pull out the big old manual for facing unhealed childhood trauma. That's how ready I was to tackle the bigger beasts of my emotional closet, only to have her tell me to go home and monitor the basics: sleep, diet, hydration, and exercise. Seriously? But I'm ready to face my demons. I'm ready for transformational healing, breakthroughs, revelations!! Come on, Doc, hit me with it! Nope, she sent me home to monitor the basics. Though I was initially disappointed with how, well, basic that sounded, I quickly realized just how miserably I was failing at all four. I barely drank a liter of water a day, my diet was trash, my exercise routine was all over the place, and my sleep habits were bordering on insomnia. Why do the basics matter? Because when you're battling a Goliath in the colosseum of self-care, it's better to be well rested, hydrated, fed, and physically fit.

Studies show that when you're sleep deprived, you're more likely to be angry, frustrated, irritable. Being dehydrated causes cognitive problems and decreases your brain's ability to function, the same way that a poor diet and lack of exercise can lead to fatigue, anxiety, depression, and a whole *WebMD* list of very serious health risks. The basics (sleep, diet, exercise, and hydration) have been proven to directly impact your mood, mindset, performance, creative output, decision making, and ability to process thoughts and emotions. So let's resist the urge to get fancy or deep with your self-care before you've nailed these down. Sometimes, self-care is a basic bitch, and we don't need to overcomplicate her. Tackling more complex items like personal trauma is not an entry level assignment. You have to learn how to walk before you can run, right? Let's be basic before we can be extra.

The Basics:
Sleep / Nutrition / Exercise / Hydration

Sleep

Get the recommended amount of sleep (eight hours recommended per night). Wake feeling rested.

Nutrition

Eat three or more meals per day.
Maintain a balanced diet with plenty of fruits/veggies.
Add/subtract foods from your diet based on how you react to them.
Listen to hunger/fullness cues.

Take a multivitamin.

Exercise

Do daily movement and stretching.
Get the recommended 150 minutes of exercise per week.
Listen to your body's physical cues (tiredness/soreness).

Hydration

Drink enough water and stay hydrated. 2.7L or 91.3 oz is recommended for women per day. 3.7L or 125.1 oz is recommended for men per day. Listen to thirst cues.

Strategy: Habit Tracking

Habit tracking is a strategy to monitor your daily habits. It's a simple way to determine at a glance whether or not you are carrying out a particular practice. Habit tracking improves your relationship with Awareness and keeps you accountable to your intentions. You can track via an app, Google calendar/tasks, or in a planner or journal of your choice. Eventually, you may track as many different habits as you wish like taking your vitamins, meditating, reading for thirty minutes a day, stretching, whatever you want. For now, track the basics just to get a mighty real look at where you're at. You might be surprised to find you may be sucking at something a little. But that's okay, Awareness is our friend. She might not tell you what you *want* to hear, but she'll tell you what you *need* to hear, with love.

HABIT TRACKER

HABIT	MON	TUE	WED	THUR	FRI	SAT	SUN
SLEEP (8 hours)							
HYDRATION (2.7L-3.7L)							
NUTRITION (3+ meals)							
EXERCISE (30 mins)							

Maintain the Basics

Once you've gotten a dose of our friend Awareness, what is going to make maintaining the basics better for you? Here are some ideas in terms of regulating sleep, hydration, nutrition, and exercise. Highlight what resonates with you, add in any strategies that come to mind, and ask yourself what would make it easier for you to maintain these four basics.

	SLEEP	HYDRATION	NUTRITION	EXERCISE
ACTION STEP	Establish bedtime/ wake time	Carry a sizable water bottle with you	Set aside time to grocery shop	Plan for a minimum of 30 mins a day of movement
ACTION STEP	Power down/ unplug from screens an hour before bed	Set reminders or alarms on your phone to hydrate	Set aside time to prepare meals and snacks ahead of time	Do a daily stretch routine
ACTION STEP	Make sure your sleep area is comfortable	Have a glass of water before or after meals	Subscribe to a meal plan service to save time	Take a daily walk
ACTION STEP	Plan for 8 hours a night	Have a glass of water on your nightstand	Schedule your meal times in your calendar	Schedule exercise time in your calendar

Routines for a Rockstar Lifestyle

Once upon a time, I used to pile into a van with a bunch of smelly bandmates and tour the country, performing at night-clubs, bars, cafes, colleges, radio stations, festivals, you name it. It was the rock star dream to live life on the road, traveling far and wide to multiple cities doing gigs. We were crammed in a twelve-seat cargo van packed to the tits with drum sets, bass amps, guitars, sound equipment, merch, the whole nine. The back half of the van was turned into a makeshift bed where I'd actually sleep. Every day was a total shitshow. Some days we'd be up first thing, hungover from the show the night before, driving for seven hours to the next city to load in for soundcheck. Other days I'd do a morning radio interview, then hop on stage to do a college performance.

My basics looked like this: Sleeping in the back of the van in the occasional Walmart parking lot, couch surfing with friends and family, eating fast food (huge mistake), getting zero exercise, and drinking more whiskey than water, I'm pretty sure. The only thing keeping me from my grave was the fact that I was in my early twenties and my physical body could miraculously withstand this type of debauchery. My point is, routine was nonexistent in my tour days. As a result, I was fighting a cold constantly. I was exhausted, stressed, and overstimulated. No wonder I had several emotional meltdowns on these tours.

Here's the thing. When your business is your art, every day is different. That's the whole fun in being a rockstar. Each day can lead you to somewhere entirely new and different than the previous day. As creative entrepreneurs, life is a freaking adventure! Getting to do a variety of cool shit is part of the reason why we get into these kinds of careers in the first place. But it makes maintaining habits that much harder when day-to-day activities vary and change.

While I'm all for you living a rockstar lifestyle, it doesn't have to be all willy-nilly all the time. Routines are essential for improving health, mental stability, emotional regulation, mood, focus, and staying connected to your biggest goals. Having a built-in schedule for self-care can help keep us feeling grounded, centered, balanced, and restored. Building a routine in a routine-less lifestyle is a way to add structure, stability, and a sense of security as you move through your creative endeavors. By automating daily self-care practices, you can free up mental space, recharge, and ensure that you don't get swept away by the whims of life. That being said, not everyone responds to routine in the same way. Explore what feels right for you and experiment with how you respond to different routines.

Creating a Morning Routine

Having a solid morning routine can be the difference between having an extraordinary day and having a catastrophic one. Whether you have forty-five minutes in the morning or three hours in the morning, whatever you do with that time sets the tone for the rest of the day. Here are a variety of self-care activities you can utilize in the morning. Incorporate what resonates and leave what doesn't, but try experimenting with different combinations to see what really clicks for you. If there's something on this list you've never done before, try it out. Then work on repeating it every day. It's important to fully try on a new habit to see if it works for you or not.

Morning Activities

- Creative writing
- Daily affirmations
- Drink coffee
- Drink lemon water
- Do hair and makeup
- Eat a nutritious breakfast
- Exercise
- Get dressed
- Go for a walk
- Journal
- Listen to a podcast
- Listen to feel-good music
- Make the bed
- Make a fruit smoothie
- Meditate
- Plan the day
- Prepare your workspace
- Pull a tarot/oracle card
- Read a book
- Set intentions
- Skincare routine
- Stretch
- Take a bath or a shower
- Tidy up
- Write in a gratitude journal
- Yoga

Fun facts about the morning: The 5 AM Club tends to be a sort of "morning glory" for many creatives. Many writers often find comfort in the early morning hours of solitude, slipping straight into the creative process before the day has had a chance to cloud their mind. Before you've been inundated with news, notifications or to-do's, the house is quiet, there are zero distractions, and there's something magical about creating while in an almost dreamlike state. Getting creative first thing in the morning can be a blissful way for you to experience your art, before your focus has been fractured or pulled into emails, texts, or social media.

Empaths and HSPs can also benefit from having a slower morning routine with minimal stimulation and enjoying the comforts of bed a little longer. For example, journaling in the morning can be a nice way to reflect and reconnect with yourself. Or, if tarot cards speak to you, pulling a card can be a meaningful way to start the day with your guides. I personally love to jump straight into Transcendental Meditation the second I wake up. Also known as TM meditation, this is a form of meditation practiced twice daily for twenty minutes using a silent mantra. After that, I jump right into my morning pages (a practice I'll explain more in chapter three). Then, I do a five minute gratitude journal to express the things I'm grateful for.

Not every morning has to be the same. You can switch it up, but trying a variety of morning routines gives you a rolodex of options to pull from depending on what kind of self-care you need. Once you have a repertoire, you can use either to set yourself up for a successful day.

Example Morning Routines

A Creative Morning

- Wake up early.
- Make coffee or tea.
- Write in a gratitude journal for five minutes.
- Prepare your workspace.
- Start writing or creating.
- Drink lemon water.
- Take a shower.

A Slow, Comfy Morning

- Sleep in.
- Meditate for twenty minutes.
- Read a book for twenty minutes.
- Pull a tarot/oracle card.
- Set intentions for the day.
- Take a shower.
- Do skincare.

A Workout Morning

- Wake up early.
- Put on workout clothes.
- Exercise for sixty minutes.
- Stretch for five minutes.
- Have a nutritious breakfast.
- Take a shower.
- Do skincare.

Creating an Evening Routine

If you've ever taken a yoga class and sweated your ass off for fifty minutes only to collapse in pure relief and bask in the nothingness that is savasana, then you'll know what exactly unwinding *should* feel like. Daily life is full of stressors, deadlines, social commitments, errands, and part of the reason we aren't unwinding fully is because we're not giving ourselves that glorious *"End-of-Day Savasana"* experience. That's what an evening routine is for. Create an evening routine that *truly* unwinds and restores you. You may think watching Netflix

85

and scrolling through TikTok is restoring you, but is it really? How can you fully unplug and decompress from the day and fully check out? Your body (and mind) needs it. Here are some evening activities I recommend. Take note of what stands out to you.

Evening Activities

- Bath time
- Cook a delicious dinner
- Do a face mask
- Do a hobby of your choice
- Go out to an event
- Go out to a restaurant
- Gratitude journal
- Have a cup of tea
- Journaling
- Meditate
- Meet with a friend
- Netflix and chill
- Plan and prepare for the next day
- Pull oracle or tarot cards
- Read a book
- Skincare routine
- Stretch

Create an end-of-day ritual that gives you that fall-on-the-mat feeling so you can actually reach a true state of relaxation at the end of the day. Your evening routine can be as simple as cueing up your favorite wind-down music playlist for twenty minutes, lighting a candle, washing up, and getting into your comfies, doing some light stretching, and enjoying a cup of chamomile tea. Whatever it is, make sure it's really relaxing and recharging you. Here are some example evening routines.

Example Evening Routines

A Netflix and Chill Evening

- Cook dinner.
- Take a soothing bath.
- Skin care routine.
- Apply a moisturizing face mask.
- Netflix and chill.
- Have a cup of tea.
- Write in a gratitude journal.
- Roll on essential oils.

A Creative Night In

- Order dinner in.
- Do a creative activity or hobby of choice.
- Prepare for the next day.
- Skin care routine.
- Read for thirty minutes.
- Pull a tarot/oracle card.

A Fun Night Out

- Meet a friend for dinner/drinks.
- Meditate after socializing.
- Drink lemon water.
- Skin care routine.
- Write in a gratitude journal.
- Prepare for the next day.

Let's Get Physical

Have you *seen* Beyoncé's Coachella performance? For some creative careers (i.e., artists, dancers, choreographers, even actors), physical fitness is simply part of the gig. Some of the world's biggest superstars are insane athletes in the truest sense. Even if you're not Beyoncé, establishing a fitness routine is crucial for your mental health. It combats anxiety and depression, boosts happy hormones, raises energy levels, and keeps you feeling healthy, fit, and strong. If your work is already heavy in physical activity (dancer, choreographer, aerialist, etc.), use this section to evaluate how you can best support your body in its recovery with things like yoga, stretching, chiropractic adjustment, acupuncture, chakra healing, whatever you may find helpful.

If your work doesn't require you to be Beyoncé, but it requires you to sit at a computer desk all day or be on your phone editing Instagram reels with your neck cranked to one side for hours on end, please, for the love of God, make sure you're moving around to break it up. Sitting for long hours daily is the new smoking. It's known to increase your chances of heart disease, lower back and spine issues, vascular problems, diabetes, high blood pressure, anxiety and depression, and yes, even cancer. Not to scare the crap out of you, but roughly 80 percent of all Americans work at a desk. Have you thought about a standing desk? Or seeking out ways to accomplish tasks that don't require sitting?

Finding a way to build physical activity into your daily routine is the name of the game. That being said, everyone's ideal exercise routine and fitness level are completely different. As you create a routine that works for you, make sure it reflects your personal fitness goals, includes your favorite activities, and jives with your schedule. If your idea of upping your fitness level right now is simply getting out for some more walks, *awesome!* There's no shame in starting small and building from there. You could also consider adding some stretching to improve your flexibility and body function as well. Take some time to reflect on what physical fitness looks like to you.

Building a Fitness Routine

1. Consider your fitness goals.
2. Identify a variety of your favorite physical activities.
3. Identify best times of day and days of week to schedule workouts.
4. Include a combination of cardio, strength training, and stretching.
5. Allow time for recovery.

Physical Activities

- Aerobics
- Biking
- CrossFit
- Dancing
- High-intensity interval training (HIIT)
- Hiking
- Kickboxing
- Lifting weights
- Pilates
- Pole dancing
- Running
- Snowboarding/skiing
- Spinning
- Sports (of any kind)
- Strength training
- Stretching
- Swimming
- Surfing
- Walking
- Yoga

Stretching

Here are some stretches to incorporate in your routine if your job requires sitting long hours at a computer desk and/or utilizing your phone, causing issues in your neck, back, shoulders, arms, and hands. Whether you're a music producer, graphic designer, video editor, animator, or social media manager, stretching will improve your performance and flexibility and decrease your risk of injury.

Upward Dog

Upward dog is a chest and heart opening stretch that counteracts the rounding of the spine that can often occur when hunching over a computer desk. It lengthens the spine while stretching the wrist and forearm muscles and strengthening the back muscles.

Piriformis Stretch

Stretching the piriformis (the flat, pear-shaped muscle located in the gluteal region) is particularly important for those sitting for long periods of time and those with piriformis syndrome, which can cause spasms in the buttock region and numbness and tingling. Benefits of this stretch include reduced risk of injury and relief of lower back pain.

Cat Cow Stretches

Cat cow is a chest opener that strengthens and stretches the spine and neck, relieves stress, and improves posture and balance. This pose creates emotional balance while stretching the

91

abdomen and stimulating the organs and adrenal glands.

Neck (Cervical) Stretches

These stretches are important for heavy phone use and/or computer work. Cervical stretches improve mobility, spinal alignment, and range of motion.

Hand And Wrist Stretches

Hand and wrist stretches are imperative for heavy mouse users or people experiencing carpal tunnel. Benefits include improved range of motion, increased blood flow to the area, flexibility, relief of muscle soreness, and lower risk of injury.

Restorative Yoga Poses

Who doesn't love a child's pose? These restorative yoga poses are gentle on the body and good for soothing the nervous system, reducing stress and chronic pain, improving sleep, and promoting mindfulness. They are easy to include in your physical self-care routine to relax your mind and body, and also to enhance your mood. You can use these poses for a five minute mental break during your day, or try including some poses in your wind-down routine before bed. Feel free to add blankets, blocks, or bolsters to any of the poses below.

Child's Pose

Kneel on the floor with your knees hip distance apart and your toes together. Lower your torso between the knees, parallel to the floor, like you're bowing down. Extend your arms forward with your palms facing down. Relax your shoulders down and allow your hips to sink into the pose. Rest for as long as needed.

Happy Baby

Lie flat on your back and bring your knees towards your chest. With the bottoms on your feet facing the ceiling, reach forward and grab the outer edges of your feet. Spread knees apart gently wider than your armpits. Rock side-to-side like a big old lil' baby!

Spinal Twist

Begin by lying on your back and bending your knees to put the soles of your feet on the floor. Draw your right knee to your chest and extend the left leg flat on the floor, keeping your left foot flexed. On an exhale, cross your right knee over the left side of your body so your hips are stacked on top of each other. Open your right arm to the right perpendicular to your body to make a *T* shape. Turn your head to the right for the twist. Repeat on the other side.

Downward Dog

Starting on all fours with your knees slightly behind your hips, place your hands on the floor, shoulder width apart, and your shoulders directly above your wrists. Press your hands into the mat, lifting your knees and gently untucking your toes on the mat. Lift your hips up and back, while straightening your legs and arms, and allowing your head to tip downward.

Pigeon Pose

Starting from a downward dog, lift the right leg up and swing it forward as if to step into a lunge. Instead of placing the foot down, place your right knee to the floor outside of your right hand and release your left knee to the mat. Keep the left foot straight back. Square off your hips and evenly release your weight into the posture. Bring your torso down into a forward bend over the leg. To come back up, keep your hands in line with your hips.

Bridge Pose

Start by lying flat on your back with your knees bent, legs and feet parallel and hip width apart. Move your feet slightly closer to your buttocks and press down into the soles of your feet and raise your hips by lifting the pubic bone.

Physical Recovery Options

Deep Tissue Massage

Deep tissue massage is typically a firmer pressure massage that targets the inner layers of your muscles through slow, deep strokes. It's often used to treat sports injuries and muscle strains, helping to reduce the tension within the muscles and tissue.

Physical Therapist

There are many forms of physical therapy when recovering from an injury. These specialists help you with a recovery plan with the use of stretches, exercises, hands-on techniques, and equipment to help relieve pain and restore function. You may also utilize a PT for a regular on-going stretch program just for added support with your regular daily physical fitness.

Chiropractic Adjustment

Chiropractic adjustment is performed by trained professionals (chiropractors) with the use of hands (and sometimes other instruments) to apply sudden force to the spine to achieve realignment throughout the body. It's often performed to treat low back and neck pain to improve your body's physical function. Many people experience immediate relief from pain.

Reiki

Reiki is a Japanese energy healing technique performed with the hands (called "palm healing") and is considered a type of alternative medicine that uses "universal energy" to encourage physical and emotional healing. Reiki promotes relaxation and reduces anxiety and stress through gentle touch. People often experience a meditative state and report feelings of peace and wellness.

Acupuncture

Acupuncture is part of traditional Chinese medicine most commonly used to treat pain with the insertion of very thin "hair-like" needles through the skin at certain points throughout the body. It's used to balance the flow of energy, increase overall wellness, and stress management.

Eating Rituals

Eating is a ritual that should be focused on nourishing your body and the *enjoyment* of eating. Eating is a routine. Too often we eat with distractions, with little to no cognizance of whether what we're chowing down on is even good for us, or we're not savoring or enjoying what we're eating. Do you eat breakfast? Skip meals? Are you scheduling your mealtimes to ensure you are eating breakfast, lunch, and dinner—with snacks in between? How much thought and attention are you putting into what goes into your body? Make eating a sacred act with the purpose of nurturing yourself with intention. Allow yourself to simply enjoy what you are eating and receive nourishment from food. Try practicing mindful eating in these ways.

Eat Mindfully with Intention

- Eat and chew slowly.
- Eat only until you are full.
- Eat outside in fresh air and/or sunlight.
- Eat without distraction.
- Engage your senses: Notice textures, flavors, smells, colors.

- Express gratitude and appreciation for your food.
- Focus on the enjoyment of eating.
- Infuse your foods with intention.
- Listen to and honor physical hunger cues.
- Notice the effects food has on your body.
- Try eating in a beautiful place in nature.
- Try eating in silence.

How can you make eating a sacred ritual that will in turn give you more enjoyment?

_____

_____

_____

_____

_____

_____

Can you improve your dining room area?
Try eating a piece of fruit by a sunny window in the morning?
Eat lunch outside on the lawn (if you have one)?
Eat dinner with a lit candle and play a beautiful piece of music?

Healthy Eating Made Simple

Here are some ways to incorporate healthy eating as part of your regular routine:

- Add a piece of fruit or a veggie serving to whatever you're eating.
- Add a "snack time" into your end-of-day routine.
- Keep healthy snacks in your car or purse at all times.

- Make overnight breakfast oats the night before.
- Meal plan once a week with a grocery list.
- Pack a snack in your gym bag for a post workout meal.
- Prepare healthy lunches and dinners ahead of time.
- Prepare snacks in bento boxes so they are ready to grab-n-go.
- Swap dessert with a piece of fruit.
- Try a weekly meal delivery service.

What Food Inspires You?

In case you sometimes feel *blah* towards meal prepping (I know I do sometimes), here are a few ways that you can engage with food that can keep you inspired and in turn provide you with more nutrition, enjoyment, as well as gratitude towards it.

- Add colorful food to your plate.
- Choose fresh and vibrant-looking foods.
- Cook something you've always wanted to try.
- Find new recipes to try online.
- Go to a farmers' market.
- Learn something new about your food.
- Try new ingredients.
- Visit a different supermarket that carries a variety of produce.

Skincare and Beauty Routines

I realize personal hygiene is *also* a self-care basic, but I'm assuming we all understand the basics of showering, brushing our teeth, and washing our faces. Let's talk about skincare and beauty routines. Apparently, you won't *actually* die if you don't revel in expensive serums and moisturizers, but for me, it's pretty high up there on the priority list, so here it is as a bonus basic for those of us that deem skincare and beauty as *essential*.

Skincare is something we do every single day. Are the products you are using doing the job that your skin needs? Are they made in such a way that aligns with your beliefs and values? Are you in need of a proper skin assessment from a professional? Take the time to find out if your skincare routine is really working for you and if you're happy and in love with the products you're using. Once you've hit a routine that really tickles your pickle, why not luxuriate in the process of taking care of your skin and make it an awesome way to indulge in a little extra self-care? You have to do it every day anyway!

Make Your Skincare Magical

- Allow the water to wash away stress.
- Infuse your products with intention.
- Light a scented candle in the bathroom.
- Place crystals or flowers on your bathroom counter.
- Play some relaxing music while you engage in skincare.
- Use a crystal face-roller.
- Use products that feel wonderful and nurturing for your skin.

Beauty routines can get a little complicated, especially if you've got a whole slew of things you find are a must in your life that need to reoccur on a weekly, monthly, or every few months basis. The trick is to identify your *essentials* that keep you feeling gorgeous, nail down how often they need to happen, and try to automate them as best as you can. (I.e., set up a regular waxing appointment, or schedule weekly blowouts if that's your thing.) Write down your current habits, your must-haves, and what you want to change or include moving forward. (See workbook at the end of this chapter!)

A TOOLBOX FOR
MINDSETS, BASICS AND ROUTINES

Use the "Rewrite the Belief" technique.

Prioritize the basics: Sleep, hydration, nutrition, and exercise.

Use the "Habit Tracking" strategy.

Create a morning and evening routine.

Build a fitness routine that suits your goals/needs.

Add stretching to your physical routine.

Eat mindfully with intention.

Evaluate your skincare and beauty routines.

Mindset, Basics and Routines Workbook

A Self-Care Basics Evaluation

Take a moment to reflect on your self-care habits with sleep, nutrition, exercise, hydration, and personal care.

Sleep

Are you currently getting enough sleep?
What may be preventing you from getting a full night's rest?
How is your sleeping area? Is it comfortable? Quiet?
Are you happy with your bed mattress? Bed sheets?
How can you make your sleep even better?

Physical Self-Care

How do you currently feel in your physical body?
Do you have a regular exercise routine right now?
Are you doing any restorative activities for your body like stretching or meditating?
What do you want your exercise routine to look like?

Nutrition

Are you eating three or more nutritious meals a day?
How often are you eating? Do you eat enough fruits/veggies?
Are there foods you would like to add/subtract from your diet?
Foods you are sensitive to?

Do you eat mindfully, or do you eat in a rush or on the go?
Do you feel in tune with your body's hunger/fullness cues?
Are you taking a vitamin supplement?

Hydration

Are you drinking enough water throughout the day?
How do you feel mentally if you are dehydrated?
What helps you maintain the habit of drinking water regularly?

Personal Care

Are you keeping up with your personal care?
Showering? Brushing your teeth twice a day?
Washing your face at night? Flossing?
Skin care? SPF?
Are you taking care of your hair?

A Self-Care Reflection

Give it a Rating: On a scale from one-ten (ten being great/one being not so great), rate each category. Be honest. After each rating, write down one action or improvement that would raise your rating up a number. (For example, let's say your exercise rating is four. Signing up for a yoga class might be your improvement for turning it into a five.) Once you have a gorgeous list of simple improvements, make plans to make 'em happen!

Sleep Rating: _____
Improvement: _____
_____
_____
_____
_____
_____

Exercise Rating: _____
Improvement: _____
_____
_____
_____
_____
_____

Nutrition Rating: _____
Improvement: _____
_____
_____
_____
_____
_____

Hydration Rating: _____
Improvement: _____
_____
_____
_____

_____

_____

Personal Care Rating:_____
Improvement: _____

_____

_____

_____

_____

_____

Reflection: Morning and Evening Routines

What activities would you like to include in your morning routine?

Do you get the chance to eat a nutritional breakfast?

Do you feel rushed in the mornings?

How would you like to feel in the morning?

What things/activities would help you feel the way you want to feel in the morning?

What activities help you unwind and de-stress after a long day?

How do you want to spend the evenings after work?

Are you spending enough quality time with yourself or significant other?

Are there any hobbies/interests you want to dedicate more time to?

Do you need to prioritize an evening workout or warm bubble bath?

Do you need to catch up with friends/family? Do house chores?

What are your boundaries with your phone at night?

Do you stop scrolling through social media by a certain time?

Do you put your phone in 'Do Not Disturb' mode an hour before bed?

Are you happy with your evening skincare routine?

Things I need in my morning routine are:

_____

_____

_____

_____

_____

Things I need in my evening routine are:

_____

_____

_____

_____

_____

Reflection: Fitness Routines

What are your personal fitness goals?
How often do you want to work out weekly?
What times of the days/nights work best for you to work out?
What are the top three to five physical activities you enjoy doing the most?

Things I need in my fitness routines are:

_____

_____

_____

_____

_____

_____

_____

_____

_____

_____

Reflection: Eating Rituals

Are there any meals you struggle to eat or prioritize?
Are you eating out/ordering in? Or are you cooking/meal prepping?
Do you have a specific time for breakfast, lunch, and dinner?
What is your relationship like with food?
Are you restrictive with foods? Using certain foods as comfort?
(If you're feeling like this may be a serious issue for you, there's
an eating disorder hotline at the end of this book.)
What would make eating nutritious meals easier for you?
Do you need a meal service? Do you need groceries delivered?
Can you meal prep once a week?

Things I need in my eating rituals are:

_____

_____

_____

_____

_____

_____

_____

_____

_____

Reflection: Skincare/Beauty Routines

Daily

What is your daily skincare?
What is your daily makeup and hair routine?
What's working? What isn't?
Are you using sunscreen daily?

Weekly

What is your weekly skincare routine? Masks and exfoliation?
What is your weekly hair-care routine? How many washes? Hair mask?
What's working? What isn't?

Monthly

What is your monthly beauty routine? Do you need a monthly facial?
Do you need a mani/pedi? Lash extensions? Spray tan? Blowouts?
What's working? What isn't?

Things I need in my skincare/beauty routines are:
Daily: _____
_____
_____
_____
_____
_____
_____

Weekly: _____

_____

_____

_____

_____

_____

_____

Monthly: _____

_____

_____

_____

_____

_____

_____

CHAPTER THREE

Self-Care for the Creative Process

I get to live this pretty amazing life where I'm actually married to my most frequent collaborator. No, really. I married a music producer and we work together all the time. (We actually met in a songwriting session, believe it or not. So cute, it's *barfy*, I know.) Not only do we work on the music I'm inspired to write, but we get to write/produce for some other incredible artist projects as well. My husband can't sing a note to save his life, but he's a total nerdy, musical genius. I may not know how to EQ every frequency to sound wizardry perfection the way that he does, but I can slay melodies and lyrics. We often coproduce together, finishing productions over bottles of wine at our home studio. He's the drop-a-breakthrough-idea guy when I'm stuck on a lyric, and I'm the vocal coach whenever he's having a tone deaf moment. This yin and yang combo of skills we possess, and our shared passion for music are what's made working together for the past ten years a total joy.

If there's anyone on the planet who knows my creative process intimately, it's this man. He's seen me laugh, cry, dance, throw things. He's seen me totally in my element. And he's seen me in the pits of my own creative hell whenever I get stuck on something and want to quit. Any time I'm like, "Fuck, this sucks," he usually says, "Well, that means we must be getting close because you literally say this every time right before you have a breakthrough and we finish the song and you suddenly love it again." And he's right. Whenever I come to a halt on something, I get flustered and say, "I'm the worst songwriter the world has ever known. I should rip it up and throw it in the trash." But I never do. And I always finish.

Generally speaking, I've learned to accept that I sometimes fall into a black pit of self-doubt and self-loathing and occasionally, that's just part of *my* creative process. It reminds me of this image I saw circulating on Instagram once and I need to show you. Because even if it sounds corny, it's true.

THE
CREATIVE PROCESS

1. THIS IS AWESOME

2. THIS IS TRICKY

3. THIS IS SHIT

4. I AM SHIT

5. THIS MIGHT BE OK

6. THIS IS AWESOME

The Creative Process

Jay-Z said that part of his creative process is to not write down any of his lyrics but rather to commit them to his memory. Salvador Dali used to sleep with a key between his hands so that when he fell asleep it would clank on a plate below him and he could wake in a dreamlike state to make art. Some bestselling authors need to rent a house in the middle of the sticks and have full-blown conversations with the plants and deer in order to write their next novel. Some actors are method actors. You get the idea.

There are a million and one ways to approach something creatively, and everyone's process is going to be a little different. There's no right or wrong way to do it except to do what really works for you. Have you taken the time to really get to know your creative process? You may think you know what's working, but then again, there might be something about yourself that you didn't know that ends up being the hidden key to taking your creativity to the next level. For me, it was learning to do my writing in the morning. My creative channel is wide open first thing, and I'm able to get some of my best work done more quickly, efficiently, and joyfully at 6:00 a.m.

Whether you need to do some yoga before you paint the next *Mona Lisa*, run a marathon before you write your next book, or procrastinate until the last possible second in order to light a fire under your ass to make a deadline (which might not be the healthiest way), my point is everyone is different. However you like to work, it's cool. Even if your creative process seems a little peculiar. Embrace your weirdness. And it's totally okay to switch it up from time to time depending on your mood, style, or personal preferences. Below is a series of questions to help you identify your creative process a bit better so you can build strategies to set yourself up for producing your best work.

What Is Your Creative Process?

How do you usually like to work? What comes naturally to you when you first start a new project? What skills are you utilizing the most? How do you like to build from there? Do you usually hit a wall of self-doubt or frustration in the middle of your creative process? How do you typically finish your projects? Or do you?

_____

_____

_____

_____

_____

_____

What Do You Need for Your Creative Process?

Do you need a lot of quiet/alone time? A big lunch break? Lots of space to move around? What sorts of materials and supplies do you need to create? Any tools, technology, software programs? What's your ideal creative environment?

_____

_____

_____

_____

_____

_____

What Works Best?

On the days when your creative process is going amazingly, what do you notice most about yourself or your environment? Were you feeling more relaxed? More confident and less judgy/critical of yourself? Were you heated with emotions? Angry, sad, or crying? Or were you working in a beautiful, serene location?

List all of the factors that contribute to a great creative day for you. Notice what key elements help your creative process work for the better. Take note of what's in your environment, and how your mood affects your work.

_____

_____

_____

_____

_____

_____

What Works Least?

On the days when everything is going wrong, what do you notice about yourself or your environment when you're having the most unproductive creative day? Note everything that comes to mind. Were you feeling uninspired and sucky that day? Forgot to eat lunch? Didn't get enough sleep? Didn't have your favorite tools with you? Or were you full of distractions from your phone, social media, emails, text messages? List any notable elements that contribute to the derailment of your creative process. Then make a point to avoid or eliminate these things altogether.

_____

_____

_____

_____

_____

_____

What Pre-Creative Rituals Do You Have?

What sorts of things do you usually require before you start creating? Do you need to set your intentions or say your affirmations for the day? Do some stretching? How do you like to set the tone? Do you need to light candles and burn some sage before you start? Do some grounding/centering or set up a crystal grid? Or is it absolutely imperative that you get a caramel macchiato from Starbucks, pack two liters of water, and have lunch near you so you don't get hangry? Note anything that helps set you up to feel ready to be in your creative zone.

_____

_____

_____

_____

_____

What Time of Day Are You Most Creative?

Notice when you do your best work and note what time of day it is. Is 5:00 a.m. the most productive time for you to write because the house is quiet and everything flows easier to you at this time? Do you suddenly turn into a Picasso when you're painting with a glass of wine at night? Or do all of your best ideas come to you on an afternoon walk? Or maybe it's at midnight? Pay attention to that creative *sweet spot.* If that's when your creative genius happens to come out, then try tailoring your routines around those times. This is the cheat code, guys! Doing this automatically sets you up for a more enjoyable, pleasurable, creative process.

_____

_____

_____

_____

_____

_____

Implement

Now that you have a better understanding of your creative process, you can set yourself up for success by building a better strategy for your creative process. Review your list of key elements that best support you. Whatever's working for you, continue to use it over and over again and ditch whatever isn't. Schedule work blocks around the time of day where you feel most creative and implement any new factors you've identified as helpful.

The top five things that are most helpful for my creative process are:

1. _____

2. _____

3. _____

4. _____

5. _____

Creative Maintenance

We all have an inner child that needs tending to. Some people call it doing things that feed your soul or filling up the creative well. I call it "Creative Maintenance." It's forever and always your job to care for and nurture this inner child. You know, the tiny, magical inner you who plays with abandon, is curious about everything, has a humongous imagination, knows no limits or boundaries, and has *fun* playing with a sense of awe and wonder.

It's the little you that loves swinging on a jungle gym or collecting shells on a beach. Creative maintenance are the practices that not only take care of you mentally and emotionally, but also put some juice back in your tank so that you're able to generate fresh, new, invigorating ideas for your craft.

Julia Cameron's *The Artist's Way* best describes this and offers some highly effective tools such as "Artist Dates" and "Morning Pages" to nurture your inner child. These strategies are designed to nourish your creativity, spark ideas, and keep the inspiration flowing. Here are some of my favorite self-care techniques that help me foster this connection. Try these out and see how they impact your creative process.

Technique: The Artist Date

The concept of the artist date is to take yourself on a little date where you can indulge in following your curiosity and child-like sense of wonder. It can be whatever sounds fun to you! For example, were you really into stickers as a kid? Maybe a trip to your local arts and crafts store to purchase some stickers and a sticker book would drum up some nostalgia for you. It could be going to an art museum or going to the beach and building a sandcastle. Julia Cameron suggested going to the dollar store with $10 and seeing what kind of silly, fun toys you can buy. It really doesn't matter. The purpose is to follow your inner child's inspiration and allow yourself to play. It can be done in as little as an hour, or you can make it an all-day affair. Write down a few artist date ideas for yourself. Give your inner little you some attention and see how it affects your spirits.

Artist Date Ideas

- Attend a class or seminar on a topic that interests you.
- Buy a disposable camera and take lots of photos of your city.
- Do a nature scavenger hunt: Take a walk in nature and collect sticks, stones, seashells, leaves.
- Draw a self-portrait.
- Go people watching.
- Go to a dollar store and buy a bunch of things little you would love.
- Go to a local farmers' market and cook dinner with what you find.
- Go to an art museum.
- Go to dinner and a movie by yourself.
- Hit a health food or metaphysical store and indulge your sense of smell with essential oils.
- Hit an art store and grab a bunch of art supplies you've never used before.
- Listen to a new genre of music.
- Make a playlist of music that inspires you.
- Make art collages out of old magazines.
- Plant something.
- Pour some extra fun into your beauty routine and do your makeup entirely different.
- Put on some lingerie and take some self-portraits.
- Read a book in a beautiful park or beach.
- Read an old journal.
- Send a care package to a friend or family member.
- Scrapbook or make a memory box.
- Take a day trip.
- Take an art class in a different medium.

- Try a cooking class.
- Try a new dish at a new restaurant.
- Try a sculpting class.
- Try an improv class.
- Try choreographing a dance to express your feelings.
- Watch a foreign film.
- Write a haiku.
- Write a scene for a movie or TV show.
- Write yourself a letter and mail it.

Technique: Morning Pages

Morning pages are a daily writing technique where you free fall, stream of consciousness write for about thirty minutes in the morning as soon as you wake up. The writing is nonstop, and you write down anything and everything that comes to mind. There's no wrong way to do it as long as you keep the pen moving and allow your thoughts to flow. Even if you're super sleepy and don't know what to write, just keep repeating your sentences until new thoughts emerge. These pages are for your eyes only, so there's no need to judge your thoughts. When you're done, it will usually be about three pages. Welcome whatever comes up, you may be surprised at what your subconscious brings forth. Morning pages are an excellent way to clear your mind, generate new ideas, receive breakthroughs, stay connected to yourself, and give yourself a safe space to vent mentally and emotionally.

Strategy: The Workation

My husband and I love to go to Big Bear, CA at least once a year to get out of Los Angeles and to change our environment, recharge in nature, and have a little bit of a vacation. We recently booked a cabin in the woods that was completely surrounded by trees, and every window in the house had a stunning view of nature—a breath of fresh air for the soul. He set up a little music station in one of the bedrooms so he could make beats, and I holed up in a small corner office to do some lovely writing for my book. I put my phone in the kitchen drawer and stayed off social media for a *whole nine days*, and dedicated my time to writing, reading, resting, relaxing, and freeing my mind of all distractions.

Not only did I get a tremendous amount of work done, but I was able to actually rest and recharge by reallocating the time I would have spent twiddling around on social media. Instead, I spent that time sitting by the fire, taking naps in the afternoon, and reading in bed. The trip was productive *AND* relaxing. It was a wonderful work trip that felt like a vacation. Thus the name, *workation*. It's a vacation—but for your work.

Maybe there's a way for you to create a workation? It doesn't have to be as elaborate as a vacation rental for a week. And it doesn't have to require a lot of money either. There's a way to do mini workations for free! Many writers often have to go away and get out of their typical environment in order to have breakthroughs or receive inspiration or focus that they wouldn't have otherwise. How can you make your work seem a little more like a vacation? How can you help your brain with inspiration, breakthroughs, ideas, simply by switching up your environment a little bit? Here are a few ideas.

Workation Ideas

- Bring your laptop to a park outdoors.
- Bring your art project with you somewhere out in nature.
- Find a new coffee shop you've never been to before that has great coffee.
- Invest in a weekend away with a short-term rental.
- Rent an office space or try a day pass at a beautiful coworking space.
- Turn an area of your home into a spa-like retreat with some nice candles and relaxing music to create a slightly different environment than usual.
- Visit a unique hotel lobby bar.

Creative Recovery and Rest

Last but certainly not least, don't underestimate the power of REST. Being creative is demanding. If you're constantly pulling from your well and asking yourself to produce work regularly, then you must be able to give yourself the grace to replenish your precious energy. All you might need is a long walk, time spent engaging in a hobby, or simply a good night's sleep. However, if you've been working on long, marathon-esque projects that are complicated and require loads of effort over a significant amount of time, you may be cranky and need to take a long creative nap. It's common to experience burnout after a very large demanding project. These sorts of things require *deep rest*. So take a vacation! Take a long break from your craft for a while, so you can sharpen the knife. If you're someone who's usually a busy body and would rather stick your finger into an electrical socket than do nothing at all, then maybe try and reframe "rest" as a crucial part of your being productive. This mind shift may help you give yourself the time off that you didn't know you needed.

What Creatives Struggle with the Most

Whether you're an artist, writer, musician, author, blogger, YouTuber, fashion designer or photographer, there are a few common struggles and obstacles that will no doubt arise at some point in your professional career, and if you've managed to escape all or most of them, then somebody please bring out the award and present you with a gold medal immediately.

What's even crazier than the fact that these symptoms are oh so common, is that almost all of these gremlins (a self-limiting belief designed to keep you safe) are actually just *part* of the creative process. For example, you may or may not be unconsciously using procrastination to get your ass in gear a week before a deadline. You may be using perfectionism as an excuse to not release that song, start that fashion line, or pitch that essay. Or you may be replaying habits of self-sabotage. Whatever it is, at times you may be tempted to sing your favorite sad song and below is a list of the greatest hits for creatives.

- Anxiety and depression
- Writer's block
- Procrastination
- Perfectionism
- Imposter syndrome
- Overwhelm
- Failure or rejection

I've sung a few of these greatest hits myself. When I was going through my depression, I also happened to be plagued with writer's block. When you're severely depressed, *everything* feels difficult. Showering and getting dressed were difficult for me at that time, so of course, writing felt pretty much next to impossible.

The thing is, I had two things happening at the same time: depression *and* writer's block. I would argue the two are closely related and absolutely feed into each other when you're stuck on the Sad Sally train. But it makes complete sense. When you're too sad to function, you don't want to write. And if you can't write (or create whatever it is you create), you feel sad, out of alignment with who you truly are, and you may even feel useless or hopeless, like you may never return to your glorious creative magic ever again. It's *scary*. But none of those things are true. Here's the truth about *all* of these sad songs. They are no different than a horrendous storm that hits your house, shakes you up a bit, and possibly moves all your crap around so you're disoriented and don't know what the heck is happening, but eventually it does what every storm does—it passes.

Here's how I kicked both my (situational) depression and writer's block.

It's important to note that in my case, I was experiencing a temporary bout of severe depression, which can also be referred to as situational depression (often tied to a major event such as loss of a loved one, major life change, trauma, illness, etc.). This is different from a chronic, long-term clinical depression that can last for years, also known as "major depressive disorder." The way to approach situational depression is not necessarily the same way to treat a chemical imbalance or a chronic depression and should absolutely be discussed with your doctor or mental health professional.

1. IT WAS A DECISION

The funny thing about my situational depression was that it felt permanent. Seriously. It was six months of hell and I thought I was going to be in a sad, immobile brain fog forever. But ultimately, I made *a decision* that I was going to overcome what I was experiencing and that I would be patient with myself in the process. I remember the decision happened when I flushed a bottle of sleeping pills my doctor had prescribed for me down the toilet because I (personally, at that time) didn't like the idea of taking pills to help me sleep. I wholeheartedly believe we have medication for a reason and each individual gets to make that decision with their healthcare provider. But for me, at that time, I *decided* that I was going to get better, somehow, some way, naturally on my own. Even if it took me another six months and I was barely crawling in that direction. It essentially took me making up my mind that eventually brought me back to my normal, happy self again. I know it sounds too simple, and almost annoying, but making that decision was precisely what turned the car around and got me out of the gutter.

2. THE SHORTLIST

Since depression literally sucks the life out of you, your desire to do anything at all dwindles, and this state of inaction actually makes depression even worse. (I know it did for me.) "The Shortlist" was a list of actions I'd give myself at the start of the day so that I had something to accomplish (no matter how small or insignificant), some achievement that would help me reestablish some confidence in myself and my abilities again. Taking action can quickly pull you out of being in your own head, so I set a goal of three to five small actions every day. In the beginning when I was really struggling, the depression was so bad that my "Shortlist" was literally only:

1. Take a shower.
2. Get dressed.
3. Take a walk.

But so long as I was able to do just those three things, I was able to say that was a win for me! It helped me feel good about myself. Eventually, I was able to add more and more to my list until I was able to get myself back to a place of normalcy again. (More on "The Shortlist" in the next section.)

3. WRITE SOMETHING, ANYTHING

For the writer's block, I made myself pick up my guitar at least once a day (which, again, might not be the best suggestion for you). Picking up that guitar to write something, anything was on my shortlist, even if it was only for ten minutes to write one little melody or one tiny lyric. If I managed to at least pick it up and play with it for a few minutes, that was a victory! Little by little, I was able to write a line, then a verse, then two verses, and then a full song! Slowly but surely, I came out of my shitstorm of depression and writer's block within a couple of months of making the decision and taking these small actions daily.

The Shitstorms and Their Antidotes

1. Anxiety and Depression

Anxiety. Wanna know something kinda cool about anxiety? The human body is this freaking brilliant vessel that's designed to keep you safe and out of danger, so really, anxiety is really just the switch that triggers the fight-or-flight response in order to keep you safe and out of harm's way. It's your body's lovely alarm system to let you know something is definitely up. (Which is pretty rad. Thanks, body!) You wouldn't want your house to be on fire and there be no smoke detector, right? It's easy to get frustrated with yourself for experiencing anxiety, but turn that thought on its head and *thank* your body for being so intelligent and communicative.

Symptoms of anxiety include intense feelings of unease, worry, or panic about future events or upcoming everyday situations, nervousness, restlessness, sweating, trembling, increased heart rate, rapid breathing, tightness in the chest, difficulty breathing, and intrusive thoughts. Anxiety may also manifest in the form of a panic attack, a totally safe but intensely scary event that triggers a series of physical reactions such as lightheadedness, intense chest or abdominal pain, tingling or numbness, nausea, fear of losing control, being detached from reality, or a fear of death or dying.

Depression is a very serious but common medical illness and mood disorder that negatively impacts the way you think, feel, and act, causing a persistent feeling of sadness that affects day-to-day activities. Symptoms include feelings of hopelessness, emptiness, guilt, anger, irritability, anxiety, or restlessness. It can also cause a loss of interest in things that used to excite you, decreased appetite, trouble thinking or concentrating, tiredness, lack of energy, and sleep disturbances. Depression can last for days, weeks, months, or even years.

While anxiety and depression are two different disorders, they are closely related, can commonly occur at the same time, and have very similar treatments.

Antidotes

- Consult a healthcare professional, therapist, or psychiatrist to discuss treatment if you're experiencing these issues regularly, and they are severely affecting your ability to function day-to-day.
- Journal your thoughts and feelings, or get creative!
- Practice meditation and breathing exercises.
- Read about anxiety and depression.
- Revisit the basics: Get enough sleep, exercise, hydrate, and eat nutritious meals.
- Take action with "The Shortlist."

Technique: The Shortlist
(Three to Five Small Actions)

Taking action is the tried-and-true way of getting out of your own head and into the present moment. Depression is kinda like a car that's stuck in a ditch. It needs some traction and momentum to get the heck outta there! Assigning yourself three to five small, manageable tasks a day while battling depression or anxiety is a way to give yourself something to focus on and helps propel you in a forward motion rather than feeling like you're spiraling out or lost in a daze. Committing to these small to-dos will help build trust and confidence in yourself and help you to start feeling better, more balanced, and able to accomplish a little bit more each day.

- Take a shower.
- Get dressed.
- Take a walk outside.
- Eat something nutritious.
- Do one work task.

List of Small Manageable Tasks

- Check in with your therapist.
- Do twenty minutes of meditation.
- Drink a glass of lemon water.
- Eat a piece of fruit.
- Get outside in the sunshine.
- Journal for twenty minutes.
- Listen to a podcast.
- Listen to a positive affirmations recording.
- Make the bed.
- Pick up your instrument for fifteen minutes.
- Put on clothes that aren't sweatpants.
- Read for twenty minutes.
- Send a text to someone.
- Send an email.
- Talk to a friend.
- Take a bath.
- Take a multivitamin.
- Take out the garbage.
- Visit a bookstore.
- Walk for twenty minutes.
- Wash the dishes.
- Wash your face.
- Wash your hair.
- Write a line.
- Write a paragraph.

2. Writer's Block

Apparently musician/songwriter Sting had a severe writer's block where he couldn't write any new songs for an entire eight years. That's a Grammy award-winning legendary icon, who couldn't write a darn thing for almost a *decade*, you guys! It just goes to show that writer's block is a very real thing that can happen at any point in someone's career—whether you're just starting out or you're already in the Rock and Roll Hall of Fame.

Writer's block can be defined as a psychological condition primarily referring to writers (but can be applied to anyone who is feeling creatively blocked), where a person is unable to produce work for days, weeks, months, even years in some cases (like Mr. Sting). It's generally described as an extremely frustrating, uninspiring, unmotivating period of blah that makes coming up with new ideas difficult or seemingly impossible. Some may simultaneously experience depression (like I did) or imposter syndrome as well. Writer's block is, however, a temporary state that eventually passes with time.

Antidotes

- Allow yourself to be inspired by stories: watch movies, listen to podcasts/music, etc.
- Change your environment.
- Do your Morning Pages.
- Go on Artist Dates.
- Have patience with yourself and self-compassion.
- Try a different creative approach or artform.
- Write (or create) a little bit each day.

If all else fails, you may need to lean in and accept the fact that writer's block may be your intuition's lovely way of going on strike and telling you that you need deep creative rest. Trustfall and embrace it.

Strategy: Try a Different Creative Process

Not everything flows effortlessly all the time. Sometimes we get "stuck in the mud" so to speak, start to question our abilities, second-guess ourselves, and it can take some real effort and determination to get back up that hill. It's okay to be frustrated, take a break, and step away so that you can receive a breakthrough. Just try not to hit yourself with a big stick of self-loathing in the process. Mmk? You may start to think all your ideas suck, or that you suck, but remember this is totally normal and that the creative process is just that, a process. It's not a linear path. Try a different route.

For example, if my usual creative process with songwriting is to start by freestyling melodies, trying a different route may look like producing a beat first, then writing some lyrics. The idea is to take the backdoor, or rather another entrance, into your creative flow so that the process itself becomes something new and a little bit outside the norm for you. Tiny switch ups like this can easily turn a block around.

Strategy: Try a Different Artform

One thing that's been true for me over and over is that sometimes I just need to engage with a different creative outlet. I may be feeling uninspired with my main artform, or I'm needing a variety of ways in which I can express myself more fully. Sometimes I paint! I usually work with words and sound, so being visual with colors and using my hands to make a bit of a mess is a nice switch up for me. The best part is I don't care *at all* if my painting sucks because I'm not trying to be a professional painter. That's the funny thing. Once your passion becomes your full-time job, it's easy to lose that initial passion or excitement, and in creeps this sense of responsibility and pressure to produce. Having an alternate artform to engage with (that isn't your job) can be so liberating and so damn *fun*! Not only does it serve as an additional emotional outlet, but it allows you the time/space to become excited about your main craft again by spending a little time away from it.

Painting a picture is going to resonate differently with you than writing a song or poem would. Using your body to explore dance movements is going to affect you differently than writing an essay would. There are countless ways to express yourself artistically. Try utilizing a different art form to tap into another part of your emotional brain. Highlight three new creative activities that sound fun to you.

Various Artforms

- Arts and crafts
- Collaging or scrapbooking
- Dance choreography
- Designing something (a shoe, a dress, a floor plan to your dream home!)
- Drawing/doodling
- Filmmaking/film editing
- Music production
- Painting/finger painting
- Photography
- Sculpting with clay
- Writing a script for film or television

- Writing a poem or essay
- Writing a song or play

3. Procrastination

This is where you leave everything to the last minute or don't feel motivated to do anything at all. It can look like putting things off or not prioritizing important to-dos. Tasks can be left undone for days, weeks, and months for several reasons. Generally speaking, procrastination has a negative connotation; however, studies have shown that a little bit of procrastination is not necessarily a bad thing. Many creatives have the habit of perpetually putting something off by delaying/postponing an action or project. Sometimes our creative genius gets activated the second we are forced to work under the pressure of an approaching deadline. I know this can be true for me in some instances, where I'll subconsciously leave something to the last possible window of time before I finally kick my ass into gear. And for whatever reason, that little extra feeling of constraint is exactly what helps me get something done. Are you procrastinating to ultimately make you more productive when you're suddenly under the gun? If you produce great results this way, it may actually be part of your creative process and a strategy/tactic that works for you. However, if procrastination is constantly leaving things undone, consider why/where it's coming from. Perhaps it's a hint that it's something not worth doing or not aligning with your purpose or mission.

Antidotes

- Be aware of when you are procrastinating and why.
- Hold yourself accountable with a friend.
- Identify what keeps you procrastinating in the first place and reduce it. (Is it Netflix? Your phone?)
- Pick a next action; choose one small task to move the project forward.
- Take a cue from procrastination. (It could mean you're not into the project and need to change priorities or cross it off your list entirely.)
- Use it to your advantage. (Use the time pressure to get things done.)

4. Perfectionism

Approximately 30 percent of the general population are perfectionists. About 80 percent of the "gifted" population are as well, which tells me perfectionism is running high in these creative streets. Perfectionism is one's tendency to set high standards for oneself, and it's likely no secret that many creatives are known perfectionists. Setting the bar high and demanding a certain level of quality in your work is totally admirable. Beyoncé does this in her sleep. But there is a line, which if you cross, it ends up being a sneaky little *b-i-t-c-h* that holds you back. Perfectionism can often prevent us from putting out any of our work at all. In fact, this is procrastination's little cousin. (They're actually related.) Sometimes they hang out and conspire together and decide to consistently postpone something because if it isn't perfect, then there is no point. Delaying something is easier than trying and failing. Labeling something as "not finished" is easier than admitting to ourselves that we might be crapping-our-pants terrified of what other people might think of us if we publicly throw our spaghetti against the wall. That is when perfectionism is not your friend. High standards are lovely. Unreasonable and unattainable standards you use as an excuse to not be awesome and prove to yourself all the reasons why you think are not good enough? Not cute. The answer to perfectionism is to determine whether you're holding high standards *or* you are just holding yourself back because of fear. And only you can answer that.

Antidotes

- Allow yourself to make mistakes.
- Commit to something you can't back out of.
- Create a list of positive affirmations that affirm your awesomeness.
- Find an accountability buddy or partner.
- Lower the stakes or risk if fear is paralyzing you.
- Recognize when it's a gremlin.

5. Imposter Syndrome

Imposter syndrome is a sense of being a fraud, a fear of being discovered as not qualified, or having difficulty internalizing one's own successes. Common signs of imposter syndrome may include self-doubt, overachieving, berating your performance, feelings of inadequacy, and sabotaging your own success. Imposter syndrome is something that can occur at any point in your career, whether you're just starting out or you're a seasoned veteran. Some people who have achieved massive success often experience imposter syndrome quickly after a hit because there's suddenly a pressure for them to maintain this level of output and status in their career. This causes people to overthink, second-guess themselves, doubt their abilities, and feel crippling pressure to deliver the same results. To combat imposter syndrome, make a list of all the things that qualify you to be in the position you're in or wish to be in. Surround yourself with reminders as to why you are qualified, skilled, capable, and able to achieve the success you desire. And remember that the universe doesn't call the qualified, but it will prepare and equip you for the call. Meaning, if you have a certain calling in your heart, you don't have to have it all figured out; the universe will qualify you along the way.

Antidotes

- Celebrate your successes: Take time to reflect on how far you've come and really throw yourself a party.
- Create another list of positive affirmations that affirm your awesomeness.
- Talk about your feelings of imposter syndrome.
- Use the "**Rewrite the Belief**" technique from chapter two.

6. Overwhelm

Overwhelm is the feeling of being completely overrun or overloaded with tasks and to-dos. You may feel like your head's going to explode because there's so much to do and there isn't enough time for anything. Everyone experiences this from time to time, and the only real way to deal with it is to decide to prioritize what's most important, cut back on obligations, and reduce some responsibilities. Be diligent with your time and remember to take breaks and take care of yourself. Can you create ways to take on less? Delegate some tasks or cut some altogether? The key to combating overwhelm is to simplify your goals and chunk them down. Focus on one thing at a time and tick off smaller tasks one by one. If exhaustion comes along with overwhelm, be sure to drop back down to the basics of self-care (ex., sleep, hydration, exercise, nutrition) and give yourself plenty of self-care activities until your mental capacity feels able to handle more.

Antidotes

- Ditch or delegate: Can you cross some things off your list or delegate some tasks?
- Identify three things that would help ease the overwhelm.
- Time Track: Track how you are spending your time. Is there anything on your calendar that isn't a priority? (More on this in the next chapter!)
- Write down all the reasons why you feel overwhelmed and how you can solve each issue.
- Write down your top three priorities.

Throw Yourself a Life Raft

When self-care feels totally out of reach, there's always *SOMETHING* small that's available and within reach for you. So throw yourself a life raft whenever you feel like you're drowning in overwhelm.

- Cancel plans that aren't a priority.
- Drink a glass of water and eat a piece of fruit.
- Meditate for ten minutes.
- Reschedule something to free up space.
- Take a power nap.
- Take a walk in some fresh air.
- Take five minutes of quiet time.

7. Failure and Rejection

Failure and rejection are both going to happen. There's literally no point in wasting time over fearing it because it's going to happen. Being the risk takers that we are, learning to deal with it is part of the process. But can we take a second to redefine failure? **Failure is an opportunity to learn.** When we redefine it, it doesn't feel like such a dirty word, does it? If you've ever tried snowboarding, then you know that being on your ass the entire first day is simply part of learning how to snowboard. The sooner you realize that falling and getting back up are **opportunities to learn** and are just part of the game, the less resistance you will have towards it. Every time someone tells you no, or something doesn't work out the way you planned, those things turn out to be either a blessing in disguise or the best ways to improve and grow. Sometimes being told no is a diversion to a different path and might be the best thing that never happened to us. As long as you keep getting back on the horse, there's always going to be another opportunity around the corner.

Antidotes

- Create a self-care plan for days you feel bummy after a rejection.
- Redefine failure as an opportunity to learn.
- Reflect on the experience. What did you learn from it?
- What can you do differently or better next time?
- Make like Aaliyah and dust yourself off and try again.

Creativity for Your Emotional Self-Care

Now that we've talked about how to tend to your creativity and deal with common creative struggles, let's talk about how awesome getting creative can be for your emotional well-being. You can use creativity to your advantage by exploring art to identify your emotions and gain an understanding of what you're going through. Unless you slow down to play around a little, you might not be allowing your deeper emotions to come up to the surface and be seen. That's what art is for. Artistic expression is a kick-ass way to process your emotions, and it's always available to you whenever you're in need of some emotional first aid. Check out these wildly cool benefits that have all been backed by research.

The Benefits of Expressing Yourself Creatively

- Decreases depression
- Dissolves physical tension
- Gives you a sense of purpose
- Helps you to understand your thoughts and emotions
- Improves ability to focus
- Improves communication
- Improves overall health
- Increases ability to problem solve
- Increases joy, happiness, and a sense of play
- Increases self-esteem
- Promotes critical thinking
- Puts you in the present moment
- Reduces stress and anxiety
- Reduces trauma symptoms

Art as Therapy

Artists often describe their art as their form of therapy. It's a place where they can release their energy and let their inner worlds come alive through art. Using creativity to express your emotions is a healthy and helpful way to experience them. Many artists are multifaceted and capable of many different art forms. Using a different creative outlet for your emotional self-care is also beneficial for restoring and recharging your main source of creativity. For me as a songwriter, if there's something I need to get off my chest in an alternative way, I'll paint or draw and use a visual form of creativity. It's sort of like getting to use a different language, and you get to say something new and different about the same emotional nerve. Experiment with different artforms to see how it feels in processing your thoughts and feelings.

Emotional Release

Let's talk about rage. Anger is a totally natural and normal emotion to have; we all experience it. Having a couple go-to rage diffusers in your back pocket could be a sweet savior from you doing something dumb or that you might regret later. Anger is absolutely okay to feel; it's what you do with it that matters. Like a video game character, I want you to choose your weapon of choice when it comes to your creative rage-release technique. Is there an activity that seems like a great way to channel all your anger? Is it wailing on the drums, doing a splatter painting, screaming at trees? Is it a break room where you get to smash TVs with baseball bats? Exercising? Or is it writing an essay or choreographing an interpretive dance? Let's find some options. Here's one of mine.

Technique: Burning Rituals

Burning rituals are something I discovered early on in my spiritual journey. They are very simple and easy to do. I write out all my rage on a piece of paper. Whatever I'm upset, sad, mad, angry, frustrated about, I write it all down and give myself permission to say *anything* that I want. I just let it all out!

Remember when Regina George in *Mean Girls* came storming into her room, screaming at the top of her lungs, viciously writing in marker a bunch of nasty things in the burn book? Yes. That. I want you to do that. (Towards whatever you may be experiencing.) Once you feel like you're done throwing a fit, then (in a fire-safe container/somewhere safe, of course), take the paper and burn it. Set that f*cker on fire!

Fire is an incredibly transformative element that will help you release and dissolve any and all negative feelings and carry them away from you through the smoke. This is one of my all-time favorite witchy self-care modalities I use whenever I'm in a rage funk. But you can also use this technique to burn self-limiting beliefs. Basically anything you want to release, write it down and burn it.

A TOOLBOX FOR
THE CREATIVE PROCESS

Reflect on your creative process.

Go on Artist Dates.

Do Morning Pages.

Take a Workation.

Take time for deep creative rest.

Try The Shortlist technique.

Reach out to a therapist when necessary.

Try a different creative process.

Try a different artform.

Choose an emotional release modality.

Try burning rituals.

Self-Care for the Creative Process Workbook

Identify Your Creative Process

Based on the exercises earlier in this chapter, recap in your own words what you learned about your own creative process. Write down how you prefer to work and when you like to work. Write down anything that helps or nurtures your creative process, whether it's being in a certain environment or having certain comforts, tools or instruments. Do you need to go on more artist dates? Spend more time reading? Have more conversations with strangers like David Sedaris? Write down any pre-creative rituals as well. Identify your creative process here.

My creative process is:

_____

_____

_____

_____

Things that help my creative process are:

_____

_____

_____

_____

My pre-creative rituals are:

_____

_____

_____

_____

How can you implement or adjust your current lifestyle to include most or all of these factors? What shifts can you make to accommodate your preferred creative process?

Adjustments I can make are:

_____

_____

_____

_____

_____

_____

What Blocks Your Creative Process?

Write down anything that blocks or stifles your creative process. Is it not getting enough sleep? Not eating? Starting work too late? Sitting on a loud subway train? Or is it fifty million notifications blowing up on your phone? Hearing the news in the background? Social media? Self-sabotage? Write down anything that has the potential to get in the way of your creative process.

Things that block my creative process are:

_____

_____

_____

_____

_____

_____

_____

_____

_____

_____

_____

_____

How can you eliminate or avoid all or most of these items so that your creative process is the most enjoyable, fun, productive, and successful?

Ways I can eliminate or avoid these blocks are:

_____

_____

_____

_____

_____

_____

_____

_____

_____

_____

_____

An Alternate Creative Process

Now that you've identified your primary creative process, how can you switch it up? What alternate ways can you create? Is there someone else's creative process you've found intriguing that you might want to try? Can you do your creative process totally backwards? In a completely different environment? Write down some ideas you find compelling or interesting to try out! Having these options in your back pocket will be so helpful if/when you get creatively stuck.

Ways I can try an alternate creative process are:

_____

_____

_____

_____

_____

_____

_____

_____

_____

_____

_____

_____

Assignment

For one week, start work at your preferred time of day, in your preferred environment with any preferred comforts. Cut all distractions, texts/calls/emails, or social media while in your creative zone. Read something new, watch something new, and listen to something new (a book, a documentary, a podcast, etc.). Go on one artist date of your choosing.

- My preferred start time is:
- My preferred environment is:
- My preferred comforts are:
- To cut distractions I will:
- The new thing I will read is:
- The new thing I will watch is:
- The new thing I will listen to is:
- My artist date this week is:

Artist Dates

Write down artist date ideas that sound fun to you. Is it going to a museum? Drinking wine and painting at night? Going to antique stores? Trying a pottery class? Collecting sand off the beach? People watching? Walking around your neighborhood and taking artsy photos on a disposable camera? In the space below, write down some ideas for artist dates. They can be absolutely anything! Try adding some that vary in time commitment. For example, write an artist date you can do in thirty minutes or in an hour or one that takes up an entire day! That way you have some options available to you if you're short on time. Let's make artist dates something that's easy to slip into your calendar.

My ideas for Artist Dates are:

_____

_____

_____

_____

_____

_____

_____

_____

_____

_____

_____

_____

Great! Now pull out your calendar and plan an artist date once a week. Try planning a bigger artist date once a month.

My Artist Dates this month are:

1. _____

2. _____

3. _____

4. _____

Workation Ideas

In the space below, jot down some ideas for a workation. Where can you go to bring your work that feels a little bit like a vacation to you? Can you bring your work to the beach? To a park? A hotel bar? Plan a weekend getaway with no distractions and really focus? Is there a city or town you've always wanted to visit? Can you bring your project there? Or, what beautiful natural scenery is available to you? Can you try working there? Write down what sounds fun to you. Think of interesting locations, environments that would be stimulating or nurturing to your creative process.

My ideas for a Workation are:

_____

_____

_____

_____

_____

_____

_____

_____

_____

_____

_____

Highlight the ones that seem the most fun to you and also the ones that seem the most easy and available to you. Make a plan to do both!

Creative Prompts

Getting creative leads to self-discovery. When you explore new ways of expressing yourself, it becomes a gateway to discover new parts of yourself. Here are a few creative exercises and prompts for you to try.

- Write a long letter to yourself saying all the things you

love, admire, and appreciate about yourself. Take time to fully acknowledge these things. Mail the letter to yourself.

- Write a letter to someone who really hurt you. Express all the rage, anger, hurt, sadness. Say everything you want to say. Be as mean and nasty as you want to be. Burn this letter.
- Take a childhood memory that left you wondering or curious about something. Write a 1000-word essay using this memory.
- Draw a self-portrait of how you feel on the outside. Then draw a picture of how you feel on the inside. Do the images match? If not, how come? Spend time journaling about your drawing.
- Put on some music and make a mess finger painting. Allow your hands to play with the colors and express what you are thinking and feeling.
- Create a fictional character in a movie. It can be a villain or a hero. If you could become any character in the world for a day, who would you become? Spend time making up the backstory of this person. Try writing a script for a scene with this character.
- Whip out your phone and take some artsy nude photos of yourself. Yep. Have *fun* taking some sassy self-portraits of yourself. Embody your sexy/playful or vulnerable side. (Keep these somewhere safe.)

CHAPTER FOUR

Self-Care While Being Your Own Boss

Being your own boss is fucking hard. You are in charge of the vision, the team, managing your time, holding yourself accountable, making money (somehow?), staying disciplined, and all of that *on top* of being a highly sensitive creator. Being the boss means you have to run the entire ship, make all executive decisions, and adapt when things don't go according to plan. Even if you don't run your own company, as an artist, you are automatically the damn CEO! As an entrepreneur, you have to take risks, giant leaps of faith in the direction of your dreams, *and* pull yourself back up over and over whenever you fall flat on your face. The hardest part (in the beginning) is finding the balance between being able to pay your rent, paying the bills with a part-time soul-crushing job, and finding time to make big moves without losing your mind. An artist's life is not for the faint of heart. We live outside of the norm, on the fringes of society, where there's zero rule book for anything. We often stay perched on the edge of an emotional high dive, ready and willing to plunge into the deep end of chaos in the name of our art. But we love it that way, don't we?

I remember when I'd just graduated high school and moved out at seventeen. All my girlfriends went off to college to live very full, structured days of class, exams, and dorm room parties. And then there was me, venturing out into the Wild, Wild West, learning the ropes of the real world, working random jobs, interning at a recording studio, networking, booking shows, and writing songs. This was the first time I realized my life's journey was completely different from most. There was no visible path laid out before me with clearly marked milestones. No road to a graduation or certificate. No friendly stranger giving out maps and directions. Nope. My trail was more of a jungle where someone hands you a machete, gives you a thumbs up and says, "Good luck." Welcome to the life of a creative entrepreneur. Where life is permanently a choose-your-own-adventure at all times. A place where you get to create your own destiny!

What's Your Vision?

So, you're in the jungle, you've decided the artist's life is the life for you, and you're about to start bushwhacking, but there's one teeny, tiny problem. You have no idea where you're going or why. And your only plan for when you get lost is that you'll maybe meet friends along the way like Timon and Pumba who'll start singing "Hakuna Matata" to you whenever you get sad and experience an existential crisis. I hate to break it to you, babe, but this isn't a plan. Let's fix that.

Step one to any artist's life is creating your vision. Before you take any swings in any direction, you need to figure out where you're going and why. Take time to ask yourself what really matters to you, what excites you, what inspires you, and what it is you really want to achieve. Then you can make yourself a little roadmap, set some goals, and start manifesting like a Boss B. Here are some top-tier strategies for getting clear on your vision. Using a combo of these methods below will help you gain clarity and get organized so that you can trailblaze your path forward to glory.

Vision Boarding

Vision boarding is a powerful practice that acts as a little manifestation magnet. If you're new to the concept of manifestation, I'm talking about all the things you intend to create, experience, and draw into your life. Some people call it the "law of attraction" or "magic" or simply refer to them as their goals or intentions. However you resonate with this concept, try creating a visual representation of your goals, dream lifestyle, desires, and intentions. Keeping these visuals on full display in front of you sends a message to your subconscious mind and puts you in your dream life, right here, right now. Feel free to put anything you want on this vision board. It could be a picture of your dream home, a new Range Rover, being on the cover of *Vogue*, doing a Ted Talk, or having a hit song on the Billboard chart. Pro tip: If you can, put yourself in the actual pictures. Go to the open house of your dream home and take a photo of yourself in it. Go test drive that Range Rover and take a picture of yourself in it. Your brain is one smart cookie. If one of your goals is to live in a ten-bedroom mansion, then seeing yourself in the picture tells your brain, *"Oh hey, that's actually me in my McMansion!"* not just someone else's random McMansion.

Mind Mapping

Have a thought jam with a poster board and some markers. There's something so satisfying about keeping it simple and being tactile by drawing out ideas over a blank piece of paper. (Of course, you can also do this digitally as well.) Whatever your big idea is, brainstorm it by drawing a big bubble in the center with the main concept in it, then start branching off into different bubbles and letting your ideas fly here. Mind mapping doesn't have to be pretty or perfect; in fact, let it get messy. Allow your brain and thoughts to literally pour out onto the page. This allows your thoughts to have a visual representation and gives you the chance to see them, interpret them, and better understand your own desires. Mind mapping is great for starting new projects, plotting your business plans, or using it for your personal self-care.

Mood Boarding

Mood boards are great for setting the visual tone, and creating an overall vibe or aesthetic for a project—whether it's for a music video shoot, your next album's art, or a fashion show! The difference between a vision board and a mood board is that a vision board is typically used for your goals and a mood board is used as inspiration for a creative project. You can use mood boards to design your business's new logo, brand your social media pages, or plan an event! I like to use mood boards for things like photoshoots, styling wardrobe looks, putting together artwork, and releasing new music. Have fun scouring the Internet for imagery and combine anything that's inspiring you! It could be photos, videos, colors, texts, or font styles. Visuals often provoke a visceral reaction and even spark more ideas in the process. Collect anything that captures your vision!

Mission Statements

What the heck is a mission statement and why have one? Your mission statement is like your internal compass: the metal arrow that will always keep guiding you back to your true north. A mission statement will keep you on track and aligned with your core values and beliefs, so that if you ever get hit with an "I'm lost" moment, you can call upon these intentions to help get back in touch with your intuition and internal guidance system. And if you get stuck in the creative process and are unsure of what to do next, you can whip out that mission statement and get reinspired and remotivated to get across the finish line. I like to think of mission statements as your pledge to the world as to what you're doing here in the first place and why it matters. It's your moment to define the purpose you've given yourself to be on this planet. Mission statements are especially important for running a business. But even if you are a staff of one, I highly recommend writing a mission statement anyway.

Write down a few short sentences that you can keep on hand. It doesn't have to be a novel; keep it short and sweet. But it should reflect the reason why you're getting up every single day to do what you're doing. The exercise itself makes you confront your own guidance system and asks yourself those big questions. What are you trying to create and why? Why is it important to

SELF-CARE WHILE BEING YOUR OWN BOSS

you? What do you hope to achieve once this magical creation of yours is out in the world? What's the meaning behind this project for you? List some core values and the things that you'd walk to the ends of the earth for. Here is an example of my mission statement for this book, *Self-Care for the Creative.*

Mission statement of this book:

My intention with this book is to inspire and inform creatives, empaths, and HSPs of their gift of sensitivity, what it requires to nurture it, and provide strategies and techniques for an artist's lifestyle, so that more people are equipped in creating a successful self-care plan for themselves. I help and empower creatives, empaths, and HSPs to grow and thrive!

Goal Setting

There are so many ways to chop this one up depending on how you like to do it. Whether you're using a pen and paper or using an intricate system of apps via your smartphone and computer, it doesn't matter as long as it's working *for you*. Let's assess first if your current goal setting method is even working. Are you reaching them? If so, yay! If not, how come? This could be the golden opportunity for you to discover a more effective way to set goals so that you will undoubtedly smash them.

Generally, I like to do goal setting in two different ways. Well, more like a two-parter. First, I like to start with setting the "**Big Goals.**" These are goals that may take you months, years, or span over your entire lifetime for that matter, but they're the goals that matter most. They are the things that if you were to perish

167

tomorrow you'd be so happy and thrilled to report that you actually achieved them and astounded yourself. Kind of like a bucket list. Then I like to chunk them down into smaller, more bite-sizeable tasks via reverse engineering or making a "**Success Map**."

Big Goal Examples

- Write a book.
- Travel to all the continents in the world.
- Create my own makeup line.
- Win an Oscar.
- Start a charity.
- Earn a million dollars.
- Build a seven-figure business.
- Write a screenplay.
- Star on Broadway.
- Tour the world.
- Design my own fashion line.
- Win a Grammy.
- Do a TED Talk.
- Showcase at Art Basel.
- Work with my idol.
- Get married and have a honeymoon on a yacht in the Amalfi Coast.
- Climb Mount Everest.
- Fly to the moon.

Let's take a stab at setting some big goals! Spend three minutes right now to write down some of your biggest dreams/goals/aspirations. (All the things that you would be so over the moon to have/do/experience/achieve.) Be clear and specific.

What are all the amazing, juicy things you'd love to do that if you were to do them, you'd be mind-blown?

My Big Goals Are:

_____

_____

_____

_____

_____

_____

_____

_____

_____

_____

_____

_____

_____

_____

Reverse Engineering

Now that you've got some big juicy goals, let's break them down by reverse engineering it. "Reverse Engineering" is essentially taking your big goal and walking through it backwards, writing down all that would need to happen in order to achieve that goal. Let's take "Fly to the Moon" as an example. If you were to walk through this goal backwards, the reverse engineered steps

SELF-CARE FOR THE CREATIVE

would look something like this: Get in a rocket, get in an astronaut suit, do years of training, get accepted into NASA, fill out an application, get a crazy school degree that's fitting for space, take all the physics and safety courses that ever existed, graduate college, learn about space . . . and so on. An even more fun way to reverse engineer is to use the "Success Map."

Technique: The "Success Map"

In Sara Connell's Thought Leader Academy, she teaches a technique called the "**Success Map**." It has the same principles of reverse engineering that makes it seem a little more fun. This is where you take your big goal and write down everything it's going to take for you to achieve that goal. Whether it's people, places, or things. Ask yourself what it's going to take to go all the way with this thing. And if you're not sure, find three people who have already accomplished your goal and write down all the common denominators they all did to achieve it. So if your goal is to become a bestselling author, reference three bestselling authors that you look up to or admire. If they all have a writing practice on most days, hired a coach at one point, or are super active and visible on social media platforms, then these are pretty good indicators of what you should be doing also. Here's what my success map looked like for writing a book.

Example: Success Map

My Big Goal: Write a book

- Create a book map.

- Outline the chapters.
- Write every day/most days.
- Do ten editing sessions with my editor.
- Join the 5 AM club to write early in the morning.
- Do market research.
- Conduct interviews.
- Write a bomb author bio.
- Book a photoshoot.
- Get amazing new author photos.
- Build a website.
- Start a blog with bite-sized pieces of the book.
- Set up a book portal and leverage the book before it's out.
- Overcome self-limiting beliefs.
- Get over my fears of being seen and being myself.
- Have discipline, hard work, patience, self-confidence.
- Network and build my community.
- Improve public speaking.
- Receive coaching.
- Decide on a publishing route.
- Learn how to monetize the book.
- Edit, edit, edit.
- Submit to a publisher.
- Be open to new opportunities.
- Prepare for launching.
- Design book boxes.
- Get active on social media accounts.
- Launch the book.

Try writing out your own Success Map with one of your Big Goals. Write down everything it's going to take to go all the way with this thing. Include internal things like facing fears or making mindset changes!

Success Map

My Big Goal:

_____

_____

_____

_____

_____

_____

_____

_____

_____

_____

_____

_____

_____

_____

_____

_____

_____

The key is to start big, then chunk it down to small. Starting with your "Big Goals," (the ones that excite the shit out of you), break them down with the "Success Map" and reverse engineer them even further into smaller steps that you can later schedule into your monthly, weekly, and daily to-do lists.

Once you have these smaller, more manageable actions, you can now activate your "**Time-based**" goals. Time-based goals are set around a particular time measurement. It could be yearly, quarterly, monthly, weekly, or daily, depending on the time you think it will take to complete a certain task. For example, if your big goal for the year looks like, "Release an album, do fifty paintings, or design a new shoe," your broken-down, time-based goals could look something like, "Record and release a song a month, do a painting every week, or design the shoe in Q1 and Q2, then market/launch the shoe in Q3 and Q4." Take time to think through how long it will actually take you to complete these smaller tasks. As we all know, sometimes the creative process takes longer than anticipated, but planning out windows of time in advance puts you ahead of the game!

List Making

My personal favorite. It's simple, straightforward, and dare I say, sexy? You can do it anywhere, anytime, on anything. In the heat of the moment, it's right there when you need it and never disappoints.

Our brains are constantly processing tons of information and in no particular order. Thoughts that sweep across your mind can occur randomly, but within them might be breakthrough inspirations, important to-dos, or ideas we don't want to forget. This hodgepodge of thoughts can look like, "I need to switch the laundry," or "Fuck, I have to pay the bills," coexisting right next to, "I have a great idea for a song title," and "I should write a book!" The purpose of list making is to easily give your thoughts a place to live so that they don't create a traffic jam in your mind. It's how you can quickly do a brain dump and free up mental space.

Whether it's inspirations and ideas or reminders and to-dos, write everything down so that you don't forget your little gems. You can keep a simple notepad for lists, write them in a planner, or jot them down on your phone. Try an app or your computer to organize your lists and set reminders to finish tasks.

Here is an example list of a quick brain dump.

- Prep for my photoshoot.
- Register my LLC.
- Finish writing chapter for editor.
- Call Mom.
- Put on a load of laundry.
- Write out a new idea for an essay.
- How can I make meal prepping more fun?
- Pomegranates could be cool for a spell.
- Who should I reach out to for writing sessions? (Names of songwriters).
- Buy a dress for a friend's wedding.
- Write a song similar to Katy Perry's "Roar" for sync.
- Apply for a business loan.

Time Management

Time ISN'T money. Once you've spent her, she's gone forever, and she's never coming back. Many of us are in the habit of believing that we never have enough time. Yet, the latest stats show that the average person spends 147 minutes a day on social media. That's two hours and twenty-seven minutes, people! How you approach time is going to be how you approach, well, everything. So let's take a look at your paradigm towards time

SELF-CARE FOR THE CREATIVE

and the ways in which you spend it. Time management will help you thrive in every area of your life simply because you're aware of how you spend time, waste time, show up on time, and create time for the things that matter most to you.

Time is also a construct. Something that can feel long or short, sort of a rush or maybe even a blur. Time in itself is almost an illusion. How do you *feel* about time? Do you have a lot of it or barely enough of it? Are there things you wish you could spend more time on and less on others? If you could wave a magic wand around and create the most perfect life ever, how would you like to spend your time every day, week, month, or year?

The way I dream about spending my time is: _____

_____

_____

_____

_____

_____

_____

_____

_____

_____

Technique: Time Tracking

Time tracking is an incredibly powerful tool that will enable you to see exactly where all your time is going, how you're actually spending it, vs how you *think* you're spending it. What's glorious about it is that you'll be able to see precisely how your time is or isn't aligning with your goals and values. Using a calendar of your choice, time track everything you do from the second you get up to the time you go to sleep for an entire week and watch where your time is going.

I like to use Google Calendar and color code *everything*. For example, my "workouts" are in yellow and my "personal time" where I eat dinner and spend time with my husband is in flamingo pink, and my "writing time" is in a pretty lavender color. That way, by the end of the week, I have a beautiful (colorful) visual of *exactly* where all my time went. This visual will tell you when you woke up, went to bed, how much personal time you had or didn't have, what work you actually got done, if you hung out with friends, did your finances, or made it to your workouts.

There's all this *stuff* we have to do that takes time that we often don't account for. I live in Los Angeles, so driving everywhere is time I never accounted for until I started tracking it. Now I have a "travel" in gray that tells me it took me fifteen minutes to get here or forty-five minutes to get there. I also have a "get ready" time whenever I have to spend more time than

SELF-CARE FOR THE CREATIVE

usual getting ready to go out to an event. Tracking these items will show you the truth of your time capacity each day. Here are ideas on what to track.

What to Track

- Morning routine
- Workouts
- Shower and skincare time
- Get ready time
- Meal times
- Work hours
- Finance time
- Personal time
- Relationship time
- Social time
- Self-care time
- Travel time
- Social media time
- Checking emails
- Responding to texts
- Evening routine

Time tracking isn't meant to make you feel like a giant piece of s-h-i-t. If things didn't go according to plan, think of it as a little mirror that is reflecting what's actually going on, then you can take this amazing information and adjust accordingly since you're now teamed back up with our friend Awareness, and the two of you can kick some ass together. If having unstructured leisure time is super important to you (it is for me) then allow for it! Slap a label on it and call it "leisure" or "the time I get to f*ck around." You have the permission to design your time and the power to manage it.

Technique: Time Blocking

Manage your time in advance by dividing your day into blocks of time. If you already know that it takes you an hour for your morning and evening routine every single day and night, why not put THAT in your calendar first? Block out all the time you already KNOW you are going to spend on lunch and dinner time or getting ready every day. Then start to add in things like important meetings, work calls, or additional social commitments. Give each activity a time increment: fifteen minutes, thirty minutes, one hour, three hours, etc. By blocking out the essentials ahead of time, you can start to see what your actual time capacity is each week. Maybe you don't have the space for that extra meeting or social engagement. If you account for everything in your calendar, the calendar will tell you what you have time for and what you don't. Spend five minutes at the end of your day to time track what happened in the day and to time block the next day.

Time Awareness

Now that you have gained this superpower of time awareness, you can now start to wave that magic wand and move things around, make things disappear, and adjust anything to your liking. You get to determine what lands on that calendar and what doesn't. Look at your gorgeous color-coded calendar. What colors do you want to see more of? Less of? How is your time spent aligning with how you *want* to be spending your time?

Look for Adjustments

Write down three adjustments right now that are staring you in the face.

1. _____

_____

_____

2. _____

_____

_____

3. _____

_____

_____

Strategy: Plan the Day or Week

Plan the day. Spend five minutes planning your day the night before or the morning of. Open your calendar and preview what you have coming up and note the primary top three to five things you're looking to accomplish for that day. Add little notes of reminders or intentions here and there. Five minutes can give you a solid structure to go off every single day.

Plan the week. One night a week (I like to do this on Sundays), sit down for fifteen minutes to plan out the week ahead. Write down your top three to five goals or priorities. Write down any intentions you may have for the upcoming week. I typically block out my work commitments, writing time, my workouts, any social engagements, and section off time for my self-care. I also love to see *space* on my calendar, so I try to leave blocks of time open to fill in the blanks as I go. This gives me a roadmap for the week ahead, and it gives me a place to refer to as I'm completing my tasks throughout the week. Weekly planning is a routine that helps me stay on track.

The Go-To Time Savers

DITCH OR DELEGATE.

I'm usually a fan of the do-it-yourself mentality *BUT* doing everything yourself can quickly absorb all of your time and energy and fracture your focus into too many directions. Ditch anything that isn't a priority or doesn't contribute to your top three goals immediately. And make delegating your new bestie. Consider delegating the tasks that make you cringe every time you think about them. Like the things you know you don't have the skillset for, or the tasks/jobs that don't have to be done by you personally. Is it time to have a virtual assistant help you for a few hours a week to knock off some of those to-dos? Time to hire a graphic designer? A house cleaner? A chef? Pay yourself back in time by paying a little extra money just to take some stuff off your plate. What about those tasks you've already been putting off for months? Can those just slip off the list entirely? No one is looking. Quick, throw 'em in the trash!

Write three things that come to mind that you can ditch or delegate.

1. _____

_____

2. _____

_____

3. _____

_____

SAY NO.

There's probably no shortage of things knocking on your door that you feel obligated to do. Taking on additional obligations takes you away from the things you really want to be doing. Eventually, some engagements become too energetically expensive for you to accept. Learn to protect your time by saying no. Turn down the things that don't inspire or excite you so you can leave more room for the things that are a giant yes for you! Saying no means saying yes to something better.

ELIMINATE DISTRACTIONS.

Unless social media time is a legit part of your workday (and it is for a lot of us), the quickest way to gain a monumental amount of time back into your day is to cut social media. Eliminate all distractions from your work zone when you sit down to start working. Put your phone on Do Not Disturb or throw it in the ocean. Adjust your notifications, sounds, and banners so that you aren't inundated with information or tempted to get distracted. Make a note of anything else that is particularly a distraction for you—TV, the news, loud background noise, alarms, noisy neighbors, etc. Try to minimize these as much as you can.

HABIT STACK.

Stacking habits is a great way to save some time. Essentially you're taking an existing habit that you already do every day and stacking another habit on top of it or introducing a new habit that you want to incorporate. For example, if you go on a walk every day, you could use that time to catch up audiobooks, make a phone call to a friend, or voice record your latest ideas and inspirations. Or if you make coffee every day and want to incorporate a morning stretch routine, you could stretch for five minutes while coffee is brewing. During my morning meditation, I habit stack by taking my vitamins and drinking a glass of water during that time as well.

Reclaiming Time with "Wedges"

Another tip I learned in Thought Leader Academy is to spend time writing in wedges. A wedge is a chunk of time that is thirty minutes or less. It's usually time we normally throw away: five minutes, ten minutes, fifteen minutes while we're waiting in line. It's those small pockets of time that you normally waste on social media or watching TV. These tiny chunks of time throughout the day can add up to an hour, maybe two! Reclaim your time with the power of wedges. Use them to write. Use them to tackle a to-do. Use them to make a list, write down ideas for inspiration, or even do some meditation or stretching. Pay attention to those little pockets of time in the day that normally get thrown away. How can you spend them better?

Being Your Own Manager

Creative people are blessed with the ability to pursue their passions and do what they love but cursed with the burden of having to be self-managed, self-disciplined, and self-reliant. Managing yourself can be extremely difficult. As an artist you are always doing three things: working in your business, on your business, and on yourself. Making your own work hours sounds great, until it isn't, *amiright?*

Strategy: Manager Monday

After almost two decades of managing myself, **"Manager Monday"** is a strategy I developed as an independent artist. Juggling both my art and building a business simultaneously often made it hard to determine how to divide my time. Enter "Manager Monday," the one day of the week where I'd put on my manager hat and do all of the manager-y things that needed to get done (respond to emails, book sessions, manage my calendar, book shows, send invoices, do outreach, etc.). Then, I'd spend the rest of my week letting my creative wings fly! With Manager Monday, I'm focused on wearing one hat for the day, and freeing up the rest of my time for making music.

Of course, it doesn't have to be a Monday; you can take this concept and apply it however you wish. Maybe it's a Tuesday or a Friday, or maybe it's simply one hour a day to handle your business. So long as you separate off chunks of time to dedicate to the business side of your art, you are being intentional with protecting your creative time. This will help you feel saner and a little more in control.

Building Your Dream Team

Being your own boss means you get to decide when it's time to hire and fire someone. Compiling the ultimate dream team is entirely up to you. As you grow as an artist and your business thrives, there will come a time when you have to pony up the dough to hire someone who'll do the job better and quicker than you can. Or there's tasks you've been DIYing for years that you absolutely loathe, and it's time to free yourself from multi-tasking purgatory and bless yourself with some peace of mind by paying a little extra money. Here's some tips on finding the right team.

When to Hire

Once you've reached a point where you've identified some tasks worth delegating, list all the jobs you're ready to pass off and who you can hire for each position. There are some things to consider before hiring someone to do any job or task. Ask yourself, *What is your ideal price range to pay for this service? Is the job you're offering a short-term or long-term gig? Is this a small gig delegation? Or are we hiring a high-stakes position in your life?* For example, a manager, new agent, or personal assistant would be a bigger role. If the job is for a position with a bit more high-stakes responsibility, then there are deeper questions you need to consider.

Compile a list of qualities and skills you'd like your ideal candidate to possess. What skills, qualities, or character traits are especially important to you? Research, ask around for recommendations, and once you find some potential candidates, review their work.

Small Gig Questions:

What are the goals you need accomplished by this person? By when?

Do you like their style of work? Is the quality of their work up to par?

What can they offer? Do they add value?

Does it seem like you would like collaborating with this person?

Do they relieve an area of your business by hiring them?

(Saves you time, money, mental space etc.)

High Stakes Position Questions:

What qualities do you wish to see in your manager, agent, or publisher?

Are they qualified? What is their experience and track history?

Are they truly excited and supportive of your journey?

What jobs and tasks do you expect them to do?

What opportunities do you want them to bring?

How are they personally and socially representing you?

What else can they bring to the table?

IMPORTANT NOTE: Always hire an attorney to review all important legal documents before signing an agreement. This will cover your ass in the long run!

When to Fire

Firing is never fun. Especially if you have to have a friendship break up. Sometimes our besties become entangled with our business in the wrong ways. (More on this next!) You know in your heart when something just isn't working anymore, and sometimes we have to learn how to let go when it's time to grow. When a relationship has to come to an end, be honest, be kind, and be clear. Shake it off and focus on how you'll level up from this experience. Here's a checklist to run through if you're considering letting someone go because what they are bringing to the table isn't cutting it anymore.

Reasons to Fire

- Dishonesty, shadiness
- Multiple big fuck-ups

- Poor communication
- Quality of work has diminished
- Sexual harassment, violence, racism
- Stealing or withholding money
- Synergy is off and not vibing anymore
- Tardiness, lack of effort, or attendance
- They are no longer serving the purpose for which you hired them for
- They are not upholding their end of the bargain
- Unethical behavior
- When their actions start to reflect poorly on you

The Pros and Cons of Working with Your Friends

What's not to love about working with your friends? They are people you like and can trust. It's convenient, it's fun; how could anything possibly go wrong? Well, plenty. Perhaps you've turned your BFF into your manager or started an entire company with them. Whatever the situation, there's always pros and cons to working with your besties. Though working with your friends can often be a joyous adventure, it's important to weigh out the many downsides as well. This is where many friendships have gone to die.

Mixing business with pleasure can be a double-edged sword. You run the risk of losing a friend and creative partner if anything goes sideways in either your business or friendship. Any number of things could go wrong. What if the drama of their personal lives starts to interfere with their performance? What if your goals, motivations, or expectations no longer match? Or they start showing up late to meetings? Start asking you for favors you don't want to do? As their "friend," do you cut them slack by understanding and let them off the hook? Or do you give constructive feedback as their boss? (You do, after all, have a business to run!) It's certainly a lot harder to tell a friend to step it up and do a better job vs. someone you've hired to do a job for you with no friendship strings attached.

As a general rule of thumb, err on the side of caution when working with friends. Decide *beforehand* what you want and need out of the relationship. Really weigh it out in your mind first and see if you think it's worth the risk. That being said, there's a spectacular number of companies that are operated by two besties, are family owned, or were created by married couples! It really just comes down to what you want, how well you communicate, and if your goals are mutual. Set clear roles and expectations, and be sure to use some of your new badass boundary setting skills from chapter one.

Building and Maintaining Relationships

Every industry is built on relationships. Networking is an essential part of our jobs if we want our creative projects to be successful. It's crucial to get out there and network to widen the peripheral. You never know who you might meet, what opportunities might transpire, what collaborators or team members you might find, or who just might change your freaking life as your mentor or business partner. And above all, make a point to follow up and foster those relationships so they can actually flourish. Expanding your network is always the equivalent of expanding your net worth.

Networking 101: How to Work the Room

Get out to some events, seminars, conferences, retreats, art shows, fashion shows, concerts, and/or hop online for some masterclasses, workshops, bootcamps, and courses. Any major events that scream important, useful, or relevant to you, sign up and commit to them in your calendar. A quick way to find these events is to identify the mavens or "tastemakers" within your industry. These are the people who may regularly throw industry events, or who seem to be a focal point in your particular field. If you were to sit down for a dinner with twelve people, mavens are like the centerpiece. (Everyone who's sitting at that table is within reach of the maven.) They're connected to a massive network and are beneficial to know. While networking, make a note of individuals who stand out to you, that you sense synergy with, or see their potential for collaboration.

Conversation Starters

1. Compliments

Compliments are amazing conversation starters. Follow them up with a quick low-stakes question. This combo is guaranteed to get the conversation ball rolling. Who doesn't love a compliment?

Example: "You did so amazing up there performing! (Compliment.) Where are you from originally? (Low-stakes question.)

Example: "OMG, I love your dress!" (Compliment.) "Where did you get it?" (Low-stakes question.)

2. Ask them about themselves

This should come as no surprise, but people *looove* to talk about themselves. And they love to feel like someone is interested in them, their story, and getting to know them. You expressing your genuine interest in getting to know someone deeper and wanting to listen to what they have to say will be heartwarming, endearing, and likely memorable for them. Hit 'em with some low-stakes questions followed up by a slightly deeper question.

Example: "Hi, I'm ___, so nice to meet you! Where are you from?" (Low-stakes question.) "Oh wow, what's it like growing up there?" (Slightly deeper question.)

Example: "Hey! I'm _____, so good to meet you! What do you do at (the company this person works at)?" (Low-stakes question.) "Oh cool, what's the best and the worst part?" (Slightly deeper question.)

Stand Out with Style

This one is my secret weapon and it works like a fucking charm. Using fashion and the way you dress or do your hair and makeup is one of the easiest ways to stand out in a room and give people the opportunity to (a) wonder WHO THE *F* YOU ARE with your sweet fashion statement and (b) give you a compliment on what you're wearing, which equates to a conversation starter that you don't even have to instigate. You can literally draw people to you like a magnet with a bold colored blazer or dress, a remarkable shoe, or a statement lip color. Use fashion to your advantage to attract people to network with. It works every time.

The Bar and the Restroom

Don't underestimate the power of the bar and the restroom. Going up to the bar to order a drink is usually the perfect holding spot to start a conversation while you wait. You're there waiting anyway, so why not strike up a conversation next to you? The restroom is even better; it's a little more private and quieter, a place where people are a little less guarded fixing lipstick, washing hands, whatever. A couple minutes in the restroom is the perfect place for compliments and low-stakes questions.

Outreach

Once you've got a few new contacts, keep the conversation going by sending a follow-up email or text shortly after first meeting them. Keep the momentum going by being timely and not waiting too long. You can also do a cold call outreach, where you introduce yourself to someone new. In this case, it's helpful to lead with a genuine comment about someone's work or another meaningful point of reference just to show that you've done your homework. You can also create a mission bridge by establishing common goals (whether it's to promote world peace, write an Oscar-winning film, or save monkeys in the Congo). Point out how you share common interests, what you can offer/bring to the table, and how you can collaborate with each other.

Get Personal

A little bit of kindness can go a long way in building and maintaining relationships. Add your own personal touch to things and be kind and genuine in your engagements. Can you congratulate someone on their new job position or latest accomplishment? Can you send someone a text wishing them a happy birthday? These small yet powerful acts establish trust and comradery, and the appreciation of thoughtfulness will inspire meaningful relationships or create opportunities if you're on someone's mind.

Do Someone a Favor

This is an incredibly impactful and memorable way to build and maintain a relationship with someone. People don't forget the favors you do for them. They will speak well of you, promote you to others, and generally just appreciate and value your relationship with them. Can you make an introduction for someone who's looking to make a connection? Can you recommend a person or service that is useful to their goals? Can you easily/quickly promote someone's work online? These small (and free) gestures pack a serious punch.

Social Media

Whether you're a company, brand, or business, or simply using social media for your own personal use, most creatives have to perform in the online space in some way. There's just no escaping it. Being visible, creating a following, and building a platform where your creations can live and thrive in the world are just simply part of the job. But staying on top of new trends can be totally draining. So how do we embrace social media without letting it trample our lives? The answer is to be intentional with your use and time on social media.

Only you will be able to determine for yourself what it is that you want from social media, and what is an appropriate amount of engagement for you. Become painfully aware when social media is becoming a threat to your time, focus, or mental health. Pay attention to how you feel online. Is this part of the job fun for you? Or is it making you want to scream and throw your phone off a cliff? Then set some real boundaries for yourself. Be fierce in protecting your mental space and be deliberate with your time online. As long as *you* are the one deciding how you are going to spend your focus and attention, then *you* remain in control.

Social Media: How to Not Let It Ruin Your Life

* Disclaimer: *If social media is consistently making you feel depressed and anxious or suicidal, it's become an unsafe environment and serious source of distress for you. Consider coming off social media entirely and/ or consulting a therapis*t.

The Pitfalls and Antidotes

Time Waster and Distraction. We waste so much time on social media. Think about all the time you've spent on social media in your entire life, add it all up, and see what you could have done with it doing something else. Gotten a college degree? Built a pyramid? How many times have you opened your phone to check something and saw an Ad on Instagram and the next thing you know, you're online shopping? Social media kills our focus and completely derails us from tasks if we're not careful or intentional. It's astounding how much of our precious time we flush down the toilet on social media when we can be putting that time towards living our best lives.

Antidote: Be intentional. Schedule time limits on certain social media platforms. Have a social media cut-off time at night during your personal wind-down time. Pay attention to when you're scrolling for no reason and when you're engaging with intention.

Trigger Warning *and* ***Information Overload***. There's no shortage of overwhelming, fear mongering, and triggering images and videos out there that can easily invade our internal spaces. Especially for empaths and highly sensitive people, consuming too much potentially upsetting content can really shake us to our core. Be kind to your brain and protect it from overloading yourself with too much information by setting boundaries.

Antidote: Curate and customize your feed by unfollowing certain content and following more accounts that provide a positive value for you. Schedule a small chunk of time in your day or week to actively seek out those accounts that inspire, uplift, or motivate you and filter out the ones that don't.

Comparison Traps. We all know what this is. It's human nature to compare ourselves and quickly fall into an endless pit of despair, wishing we had what other people have. Comparing ourselves to anyone else is a complete waste of time because while you're wishing and envying, you *could be* focusing that energy on you, your path, your goals. Rather than feeling like crap over someone else's success, can you congratulate them? And know that their success takes nothing away from your own?

Antidote: Either unfollow accounts that make you feel like crap OR congratulate people and say to yourself, "I am one with that." When we see people winning at something that we want, it's a strong indicator of our desires, dreams, and goals. Rather than feeling shitty and thinking someone else's success is our loss, "I am one with that" is a way for you to acknowledge this desire within yourself and believe that it's also *possible* for you too. When you say this mantra, you are energetically saying, "If the universe can bless this person this way, then the universe can also bless *me* this way." You are yessing your own success! (Rather than separating yourself from it.)

Content Fatigue. Remember, you are human, not a machine. Creating content and managing social media accounts takes up a lot of time and energy. Content fatigue is real and means you maybe need a break when you're feeling particularly uninspired and drained.

Antidote: Rest and reconsider your content creating schedule to better suit the needs of your mental health. Consider hiring a social media strategist or social media manager to take off some of the mental load for you.

Trolls. The Internet is full of f*cked up trolls, who have nothing better to do than to sit online and trash talk others. Hurt people hurt people. Some people feed off drama by spewing novels in the comments by getting into large debates. Unfortunately, this is the only way some people feel powerful, important, and relevant (by shitting on others).

Antidote: Whenever you get hate, just send those little trolls some love and compassion and say to yourself, "You know what, that person must feel so bad about themselves on the inside, which is why they need to cut people down online. How sad for them. I wish you well, troll!" Take nothing personally, and don't engage.

Occasionally, a clapback may be totally warranted. It can be a boss move to make an example out of someone to raise awareness on social or political or racial issues that are important to you. If you strongly feel the need to raise your voice about it, by all means! So long as it's a) authentic to you and b) still protecting your energy. Otherwise, you don't have time to engage with trolls and can't afford to energetically stoop to their level. If some trolls are invading your mental space, consider blocking them entirely. And mooove on, honey! Focus on all the awesome things social media CAN do for you.

The Plus Sides of Social Media

- You can make a lot of money.
- You can work with brands you love and support.
- You get to be creative and have fun on your platform.
- You get to be visible.
- You get to learn from others.
- You get to make new connections.
- You get to meet your ideal audience and build a community.
- You get to promote all your amazing projects!
- You get to use your voice, share your message, and inspire others.

Strategy: Develop a Code of Conduct

People often complain about social media, saying how much they hate doing it, or it's too hard to keep up with all the trends, etc. But what if you could just throw the entire concept out the window and make social media a *freaking party*? Seriously, how can you make engaging in social media actually fun and pleasurable for yourself? 'Cause if it's not fun for you, is it really going to work for your business if you're dreading everything?

Develop your own personal code of conduct of how you choose to engage online. Your code of conduct could look like this:

1. I only post content that I enjoy making and am totally passionate about.
2. If I want to poke my eyes out, I'm getting off social media.
3. If it's not fun, I don't do it.

Try writing down three things that are in your personal code of conduct towards social media:

1. _____

_____

2. _____

_____

3. _____

_____

Creating these personal rules can put some serious power back in your hands, *and* push you to be even more authentic online (which is what your audience wants from you anyway). It's a win-win.

Strategy: Schedule Content Creating Time

Creating content for your social media platforms may be a huge and integral part of your job. Set boundaries by scheduling designated content creating time. Carve out time in your calendar in advance for specific content creating blocks. Perhaps you need additional editing time? Schedule out time for that piece as well. Once that time block is up, stop, and take a break before coming back to the next chunk of the scheduled time.

Money

Shall we switch gears? Let's talk money and how to self-care the f*ck out of your finances. We're all in the business of making some dinero with our art, which can feel . . . *icky* sometimes. But it doesn't have to. Before we go any further, let's all take a collective breath and sigh it all out. Because this next part will require you to take full responsibility for where you're currently at. Maybe your finances are going great, or maybe they suck ass right now. Wherever they're at, take full, whole-hearted accountability for them, so you can step in, step up, and take charge.

What Are You Believing About Money?

We attract whatever it is we are believing about money. If money always seems to evade you, leave you, or never come to you, chances are you have some heavy resistance towards money, which means you are hanging on to some belief systems about money that obviously aren't serving you. Let's take a peek, shall we?

Write down everything you believe about money:

_____
_____
_____
_____
_____
_____
_____
_____
_____
_____
_____
_____
_____
_____
_____

Where did these beliefs come from?

_____
_____

_____

_____

_____

_____

_____

_____

_____

_____

_____

_____

_____

_____

Revisit the "**Rewrite the Belief**" technique from chapter two.

Technique: Money Tracking

Track your finances so you can take a look at your spending habits and keep an eye on your money. Similar to time tracking, use a money tracking system that works for you so you can see exactly where all your money is going. Sit down with your finances at least once a month. Actually _look_ at your spending. Are you eating out way too much? Going out too often? Is it in line with your personal values? Or is your shopping getting a little out of hand? Are you able to save or invest? Perhaps you have some debt to crush. Whatever it is, you can't improve your finances unless you become fully aware of your financial picture and take ownership of it. So get tracking!

Technique: Tracking Abundance

Thought Leader Academy offered a five-week program called the "Abundance Accelerator" where a group of about twenty-five women collectively generated over 1.1 million dollars within the five weeks. Something we did each week was write down at least five actions we thought could generate more money or lead to an opportunity that would lead to more income. It could be sending emails to potential clients, creating a pitch deck for a new creative service, or launching a website. Five actions—small or big. I called them "Abundance Actions." (All the things I'd take action on that could potentially lead to more income.) And as part of my end-of-day routine, I tracked any abundance of actions I took that day, income that occurred, and any financial miracles that came my way because whatever you track *increases.*

A TOOLBOX FOR
BEING YOUR OWN BOSS

Use vision boards, mind maps, and mood boards.

Write a mission statement.

Try writing out your Big Goals.

Try the Success Map technique.

Use list making.

Time track and time block.

Try the strategy Manager Monday.

Ditch or delegate.

Habit stack.

Use "wedges" to reclaim time.

Develop a social media code of conduct.

Track abundance.

Self-Care While Being Your Own Boss Workbook

Mission Statement

Write a three-line mission statement that encapsulates what you're doing and why. State concisely what value you bring to the table, what makes you different, and what your aim is. Include a brushstroke of your core values and beliefs.

My Mission Statement:

_____

_____

_____

_____

Your Big Goal x The Success Map

Review what you wrote down in your "Big Goals" list. Is there one in particular that you are currently focusing on right now? Is there one you want to start? Choose one of your "Big Goals" and run it through "The Success Map."

My One Big Goal Is:

_____

_____

_____

_____

The Success Map

Reflect on your one "Big Goal" now and write down everything that it's going to require to take this goal all the way to the finish line. Think of people, places, or things you might need. Any self-limiting beliefs you might need to overcome? Relationships you need to attract? Skills you need to acquire? What's it going to take?

For inspiration, find three people who have already achieved the same goal and write down how they did it.

To Achieve My Big Goal of_____, It Will Take:

_____

_____

_____

_____

_____

_____

_____

_____

_____

_____

_____

_____

_____

_____

_____

_____

_____

_____

_____

_____

Time Tracking

Identify and list all of your "Time Categories" that you will be tracking and give them a color that resonates with you. List all the major activities you currently spend the most time on and add the minor activities that also tend to fill up the day. Here is an example.

MAJOR TIME CATEGORIES	MINOR TIME CATEGORIES
Work hours (Blue)	End-of-day routine (Green)
Creative hours (Blue)	House chores (Gray)
Business hours (Blue)	Daily travel (Gray)
Personal hours (Pink)	Planning the week (Green)
Writing time (Lavender)	Morning/evening routine (Pink)
Leisure time (Yellow)	Get ready time (Pink)
Meetings or calls (Blue)	Meal prepping (Green)
Unstructured time (Yellow)	Workouts (Yellow)
Self-care time (Pink)	Social time (Yellow)
Family time (Red)	Finances (Green)

Write out your major and minor time categories here and give them a color so you can track them on your calendar.

MAJOR TIME CATEGORIES	*MINOR TIME CATEGORIES*

Reflection: Time Adjustments

Reflect on how you can adjust the ways you spend your time. Let's do this in two categories: immediate changes and dream changes.

Immediate Changes: Write down any immediate changes you'd like to see in regards to your time. Do you have a desire to get up earlier to work out? Want to cut back on some TV time? Want to spend more time reading? Whatever it is, write down what you want more or less of.

_____
_____
_____
_____
_____
_____
_____
_____
_____
_____
_____
_____
_____
_____
_____

Dream Changes: Write down your absolute ideal way of spending your time on planet earth. What would your dream life look like 365 days a year, 7 days a week, 24 hours a day? Are you vacationing twice a year? Working 4 days a week? Being creative all day on a private island? Have some fun here and imagine your dream life and the way you spend your time.

_____
_____
_____
_____
_____
_____
_____
_____
_____

_____

_____

_____

_____

_____

_____

_____

_____

_____

_____

Time Adjustments and Solutions: Using two columns, write down all your "Time Adjustments" in the left column. In the right column, write down a solution for solving or implementing each of them.

TIME ADJUSTMENTS	*SOLUTIONS*

Example: Time Adjustment	*Example: Solution*
I need one more hour in the morning.	I will get to bed one hour earlier.

I have an engagement that isn't a top priority.	I will cancel or reschedule.
I have too much on my plate at work.	I will delegate some tasks.
I have no time to grocery shop.	I will have my groceries delivered.

Reflection: Social Media

Write out your own personal code of conduct with social media. These are your personal rules and boundaries that you will set for yourself, so that engaging online remains a healthy and safe space for you. Write out your own set of rules for social media.

_____

_____

_____

_____

_____

_____

_____

_____

_____

_____

_____

_____

_____

ACTION: Unfollow five accounts whose content is not serving you. Follow five new accounts whose content you are inspired by, feel motivated by, or are learning something from.

Reflection: Money

Abundance Actions: Write out five abundance actions that you can take this week that could potentially lead to generating more income for you. For example, email five new potential clients for your business, do outreach to potential collaborators, brainstorm a new program idea you can sell, or start building a website. Then do them!

_____

_____

_____

_____

_____

_____

_____

_____

_____

_____

_____

_____

_____

_____

_____

_____

_____

_____

CHAPTER FIVE

Self-Care for the Creative Home

I remember binge watching the Netflix show, *How to Make a Sexroom*, where a lovely English woman whose profession is interior design, takes her decor skills and applies them to making "sex rooms" for couples. The combination of design, sexuality, and intention is what made it altogether too easy for me to completely devour this show in a night. How fun! To dedicate an entire room to your pleasure and personalize it to your specific wants, needs, and personal style? I couldn't look away. Shortly after my TV binge, I was wildly inspired to spice up my own bedroom and see how I could make my boudoir a little sexier up in there!

Upon walking into my bedroom, I took note of a few things that immediately made me cringe. The first thing that HAD to go was laundry. The sight of any towels half-assedly not making it into the basket screamed, "CHORES!!" at me—the most unsexy energy ever. Books and journals scattered across my bedside table, crystals and oils clustered on my dresser. Clutter poking me directly in between the eyeballs. It looked like a physical expression of my intellect spiraling out in a place that's supposed to be . . . chill? If I wanted my bedroom to inspire sexy time, some things needed to change. Not only that, but I needed it to be a place where I could unwind, connect with my husband, and get a comfy, cozy, restful sleep.

I closed my eyes and connected to the *feeling* that I wanted from this room. I used my imagination to drum up any ideas about how I wanted the room to function, what mood lighting I could introduce, or what decor shifts I could make. I took note of any and all inspirations and intuitions that served my intentions with the room.

In a day, I quickly transformed our bedroom by ditching the laundry, removing all the clutter, and picking up a few new pieces of decor that inspired and evoked the feeling that I was craving—like intimacy, playfulness, and connection. I picked out one of my favorite lingerie outfits to hang on the wall as a decor piece on a gorgeous gold hook. I added a soft, lush throw blanket that begs you to come lie on it. On the dresser, I put sex toys on full display in a fancy glass tray. Candles went *everywhere,* and just to be dramatic, I purchased a tiered fruit tray and a champagne bucket to occasionally whip out the bubbly and chocolate strawberries. Yes, this took it to a whole other level and was much more inviting for me to connect with my husband. These super subtle, inexpensive additions made *such* a difference in how I felt and changed the way I behaved (or didn't behave) in my bedroom. This is just one example of how your home (and what you put in it) can directly influence your mood.

Home Self-Care

Your home is your sanctuary. It's somewhere you eat, sleep, relax, have sex, recharge, and for many creatives, it's also where we work and exercise. It's astounding what we demand from our personal spaces. Our environments have a tremendous impact on us, whether we know it or not, especially as empaths and HSPs. The objects that you keep around you have energy and the power to spark a feeling, a thought, or an emotion. Clutter and disarray can completely paralyze you, cause stress within your physical body, or distract you. A messy closet or disorganized pantry has the potential to block the flow of energy in your home and in your mental space as well. Because creatives often work from home, the home must function and serve more purposes, which can be challenging. The home is not only your place to relax, but it's also your place of work. All the more reason to make your home the bomb dot com!

Since we are so affected by our environments, why not transform our home environment into a place that's as blissful as possible? A place that inspires your greatest work every time you sit down to create? If you're a creative person who's spending 99.99 percent of your time at home, *why not make it a freaking sanctuary?* Take time to do a little home self-care to make sure your home is accommodating your workspace and offering a restorative place for you to unwind.

Do a Home Audit

Remember our dear friend, Awareness? Well, she's coming over right now with Starbucks to help you walk through your closet and make a few decor suggestions. Doing a complete home make-over can feel like a daunting and overwhelming experience. Take a deep breath and let her walk through your home and ask you some questions. And know that you don't have to tackle everything in a day.

Do a home audit by walking into every room in your house and make a note of what your first impression is. What you like, what you don't like, what you wish to see differently, what are the eyesores? What is bothering you or impacting you negatively? Take stock of any thoughts or emotions that arise during this process. What needs are coming up? Do you need to spend a day properly organizing things? Purge some items you no longer love or use? How does your house feel clutter-wise? Are there any spots in the home that are giving borderline hoarders? When you open your closets, do you want to scream? Is there crap all over your kitchen counter that's making it feel *not* dream-homey? Scan through every area of your home quickly and catch anything of note. How are the surfaces of your coffee table, work desk, or dressers? How are the drawers? Note how you feel about your space. Write down anything that is physically or mentally bothering you, and let's get them under control.

My Home Audit

Bedroom

Problem Areas: _____
_____
_____
_____
_____
_____
_____
_____
_____
_____

Changes/Solutions: _____
_____
_____
_____
_____
_____

_____

_____

_____

_____

Bathroom

Problem Areas: _____

_____

_____

_____

_____

_____

_____

_____

_____

Changes/Solutions: _____

_____

_____

_____

_____

_____

_____

_____

_____

Work Area

Problem Areas: _____

_____

_____

_____

_____

_____

_____

_____

_____

Changes/Solutions: _____

_____

_____

_____

_____

_____

_____

_____

_____

Closets

Problem Areas: _____

_____

_____

_____

_____

_____

_____
_____
_____
_____

Changes/Solutions: _____

_____
_____
_____
_____
_____
_____
_____
_____

Kitchen

Problem Areas: _____

_____
_____
_____
_____
_____
_____
_____
_____

Changes/Solutions: _____

_____
_____
_____

_____
_____
_____
_____
_____
_____

Living Room

Problem Areas: _____

_____
_____
_____
_____
_____
_____
_____
_____

Changes/Solutions: _____

_____
_____
_____
_____
_____
_____
_____
_____

Spring Cleaning

Your physical environment always reflects the person that you are and the person you are becoming. So why not create the environment of the person you are striving to be? Does the rich millionaire you desire to be wear that old ratty sweater? Probably not. Does the healthy, fit yoga guru have an unbearably disorganized pantry? Hell no. Every area of your home can become a direct expression of who you want to become.

Our identity is a direct reflection of the things that we own or hold on to.

Spring cleaning is so much more than just getting organized. It creates an energy flow in your home and is a way to ensure that everything you own has a purpose or a function. When things start to feel cluttered, disorganized, or out of place, it will affect you psychologically. Whatever state you're currently in mentally/emotionally will be seen within your surroundings, so it's an incredible opportunity for you to check in with yourself and see what you're manifesting. (For the record, you can spring clean any time of year!) But the idea of a spring clean is to do a deeper cleanse and get rid of anything that is no longer serving you or in alignment with who you are. Clean out what doesn't need to be occupying space in your home.

Objects have energetic weight to them. When you ditch the things that you've outgrown and that aren't correctly representing you anymore, it becomes a therapeutic release. Physically and mentally, you'll actually feel *lighter.*

Pick an area of your home and walk through all of your items.

Are they "sparking joy" like Marie Kondo said?

Are they useful or serving a purpose?

Are they a reflection of the person you are or wish to become?

Are they sentimental?

If you're a sentimental person and have a hard time letting go of things, that's cool. Give yourself a sentimental box or bin where you're allowed to keep a few special items just for shits and gigs. Or alternatively, you can turn sentimental items into decor pieces that you can display! Are your dad's old skis something you can hang on the wall? Or is your grandma's fruit bowl a great way to store some paint brushes? Allow yourself a "sentimental" pile if so. Besides "keep," you have three options when it comes to spring cleaning:

DITCH.
DONATE.
SELL.

Things that have holes in them go immediately in the trash. Wearable but no longer loveable by you has "donate" or "sell" written all over it. Sure, things can be repurposed, reused, or recycled, but be ruthless. You either ditch, donate, or sell. Be freaking honest too. When you're holding up that pair of jeans you bought over a year ago, but you never wore, saying, "Maybe one day I'll feel inspired to wear them" or "These are brand new!" or "I think I like it . . ." then it's probably not sparking enough joy for you and maybe, just maybe . . . you're lying to yourself just a lil' bit and it's time to let it go. Every item you hang on to is either a YES to your future self, or clinging-on to some past version of yourself that we all know you should probably outgrow already. Your choice in things is like setting intentions for who you want to be.

How to Declutter

Try decluttering an area of your home by wiping the slate totally clean and starting from scratch! Let's take your kitchen for example. Pull everything off the kitchen counters and place it in a staging area for you to start making some decisions about what stays and what goes. You can do your cupboard and drawers as well if you wish, but start from zero so you can slowly start putting back what's most important to you. The key to decluttering is that less is more. Make sure that the items you put back are working, useful, or serving a purpose, and arrange them in such a way that it is visually pleasing to you and you *feel* good being in that area of your home. Anything old, broken, or not serving a purpose has got to go. Anything that has bad energy, like the coffee mug your ex gave you, needs to become friends with the trash. Once you've arranged the topical surface area in a way that's pleasing to the eye, suits your needs, and functions, you can move on to the aspects of organization inside cupboards, drawers, and any other nooks and crannies.

Get Organized (Like the Home Edit)

Who didn't watch an episode from *The Home Edit* during the pandemic? Pretty sure I binged that whole show and went straight to The Container Store and dropped some serious cash on organizational supplies because turning my whole house upside down was one of the most appealing projects and pastimes during lockdown. Here are my favorite moves from *The Home Edit* that are beyond transformative to your personal space.

Move #1: Capitalize on vertical wall space.

Especially for tighter spaces, make the most of all that wall space by installing a unit that you can use for storage or hanging items where you can easily grab and utilize them.

Move #2: Organize with bins, baskets, and labels.

Slap a label on a basket or bin so you can easily store and locate particular items in your home without having to go digging.

Move #3: Arrange colored items according to the rainbow.

Got a bunch of colored markers or books or a crystal collection kicking around? Cool, try arranging them according to the colors of the rainbow for a super visually pleasing look.

Express Who You Are with Decor

Once you've worked on some decluttering and organization, how can you make your environment pop with more *you* in it? The items we purchase and put on display say a lot about who we are and what we value, as well as reflect our own personal style and taste. Show off your personality a little through your decor! Are you obsessed with plants? Little figurines? Wall art? Love gold accents? Or do you love antiques? Candle holders? Mid-century modern furniture? Do you have any items that are sentimental or important to you that you'd love to display? There is so much you can do in terms of tailoring your space so that it's functional and showcases who you are. Noticing what we like in terms of objects, colors or textures is a good way to get started building an interior style. Pay attention to any details that you are drawn to.

Working from Home

Once upon a time, I rented the tiniest room ever for $500 a month in a house located in East Vancouver where I lived with three boys as roommates. My room wasn't even big enough to fit a bed, or if it did, it would have taken up the entire room. Instead, I chose to put a small foamy bed on the floor (so sad, I know), that way I could at least set up a small makeshift area where I could set up my keyboard, my laptop, and my speakers so I could make beats and record my music. I chose being able to make music over a freakin' bed. Obviously this was shitty for many reasons.

1. I didn't have a bed.
2. I was completely cramped recording in one corner of my "room" and barely sleeping in the other.
3. It felt like a prison cell.

But the reality for me at the time was that I needed cheap rent, and I needed to be able to make music on my cheap rent, so sleeping on a three-by-six cut-out foamy is what I did. And it made me feel like a sardine in a single sardine can.

Flash forward years later, I was living in a one-bedroom apartment in Brooklyn, where I was able to set up a real desk for all my music equipment. It even had a big, beautiful window that overlooked the street. My work desk was adjacent to the living room area and within view of the kitchen. While this work setup was a serious upgrade from where I'd been living just a couple years prior, I found that whenever I was cooking dinner, I'd be thinking of emails I hadn't responded to, and when I was sitting on the couch watching TV, I'd be tempted to open that song real quick to finish it because my computer was right there staring me in the face. There was no separation from my work desk and the rest of my apartment. What do you get when you put "home" and "work" so close together like that? *Homework.*

Now I have the lovely advantage and luxury of a "home office." An entire studio/office that's detached from the house, where I can fully dedicate myself to my work in a single designated area. Since I've lived through varying degrees of working arrangements from home, I have insights for all of them. Whether you've got roomies, one bedroom to yourself, or an awesome workspace for yourself at home, I can offer tips for all of these options. I gotchu.

Creating a Workspace or Home Office

Give yourself permission to fill up your workspace with whatever inspires you and helps you feel like your best creative self. Make a mood board with some styles you find on social media. Take a flip through some home decor magazines or browse through your favorite home decor shops online. Or if you happen to go to a restaurant or over to a friend's house and see something you like, take a photo of it! Take a minute to write about your ideal workspace right now. What's in it? What does it make you feel? What colors or objects do you see? What style of furniture?

My ideal workspace looks like:

_____

_____

_____

_____

_____

Make your workspace magical by decorating it with anything that helps get your creative juices flowing! Maybe your desk has fun stationary on it and your vision board nearby. Try adding some plants to your office or some new decor pieces that spark some inspiration in you. Have fun adding quirky items that express your personality. I like to keep word blocks with daily inspirations on them, pictures, post-its, plants, candles, crystals, and sage around me at all times. But that's me! Experiment with whatever feels good to you.

How to Not Go Insane Working from Home

This comes with a variety of challenges, including creating your own structure for the workday, remaining disciplined and motivated, and maintaining healthy home/work boundaries. Working from home can often mean working alone, depending on what you do, of course. Not to mention the possibility of not seeing another human soul for the entire week! Living a solitary work life, which many creators do, can be super difficult and hard on you without you even realizing it. Here are some things to look out for and/or implement into your at-home workspace to keep a sense of balance and your mental health in check!

Create Separation

As many of us experienced during the COVID-19 pandemic, kitchen tables became offices, bedrooms became boardrooms, and our basements became the headquarters of creative businesses! Adjusting our home to fit our workplace needs is a self-care process all on its own! Tip number one is to create separation between where you work and where you unwind. If you're fortunate enough to have a separate room in the house for your work, or even a separate studio space, then this'll be a little easier for you. But let's say you're renting a bedroom in a house with roommates where your work desk is crammed right beside your bed where you sleep at night. (I totally get it.) Is there a divider you can add to your room? Or a goofy little sign that sits on your desk that says "Open for Business" and flips to "Closed for Business" for when you're done for the day? Give yourself something, anything that sends a signal to your brain that *this* is where I work and *that* is where I relax, unwind, and hang out.

No matter what you're working with, creating a sense of separation between your work premises and where you relax at home is key to a healthy work/life balance. It can be difficult to check out from work if you're sleeping next to your computer or it's staring you down at the dinner table, probing you to respond to a few more emails. What would it take for you to create a separate workspace for yourself? If you're working with a small space, would you consider a room divider or rearranging the space slightly differently so it feels a little more sectioned off? Or use a curtain? Whatever you can do to create a physical separation from your work office and the place where you sleep/eat/relax, do it!

Get Dressed Like You're Going to a Job (Sometimes)

It's way too easy to wear sweatpants all day every day while working from home. Seriously. Unfortunately, doing that permanently isn't cute for anyone, and it does start to creep in on your subconscious self-esteem and tamper with your overall self-care. Plus, you'd be amazed at how much better your work is when you're dressed up and feeling like the confident boss that you are. People who show up to work in an actual office have to dress up every day, so why not continue to show up for yourself with the same seriousness and professionalism? You are, after all, a creative professional, so tell your brain that by getting dressed! (Even if it's just for yourself.) Make sure that on some days of the week, you're doing your hair and makeup, and putting on real clothes that make you feel like a boss. See how that affects your confidence (and work) throughout the day.

Take a Break (Outside)

Working from home can feel like you're just in your little cave all the time, so take a break and get outside for some fresh air. Go somewhere, anywhere. Get a coffee, run some errands, take a walk, get some sun. When you're working throughout the day, make sure you're getting up, moving around, and taking breaks here and there to keep the blood flow going. Little breaks will keep you energized, and fresh air is synonymous with new ideas striking your brain like lightning. You can even schedule these little breaks by setting alarms on your phone every hour so you can at least stand up. Or schedule a walk around the block as part of your after-lunch routine.

Create an End-of-Day Routine

I can't stress this one enough. Create an end-of-day routine for when you're done working. "Clocking out" can be hard to do when you work from home. It may be tempting to keep working when you're "off" and it can become difficult to unwind in your home when you're done. It takes a minute for the brain to compute that you are no longer in work mode and switch over to being off and in relaxing mode. Do something physical or tangible that can help shift your mental state out of your work zone and into your evening routine. It could be as simple as turning off all the lights in your office, powering down your computer, and going for a walk, or putting on a pot of tea and sipping that tea for ten minutes.

Play with different sequences of activities to see what best helps your brain clock out for the day. This will help create a boundary between your "work life" and your "home life." And when you are done for the day, BE DONE. Make an agreement with yourself that you have specific work hours and specific chill-out hours. Be fierce in protecting your off time, because you really do need it to recharge. If you still continue to struggle with "clocking out," try adding a disruptor at the end of your day. A disrupter is a commitment that requires you to leave the house and physically pulls you out of your "workday," such as going to a workout class or going to dinner with a friend. You'll be mentally out of the office in no time.

Don't Just Stay In Your Little Hole: Get Social

Make time for your social life. Working from home is where your social life may go to die. We are social creatures by nature so 1,000 percent make this a priority. The solitary work lifestyle makes it easy to go an entire week without seeing a single soul or having a decent conversation. If this is you, then perhaps adding a social calendar to your weekly time blocking is a good tool for you. Every month and/or week sit down and start scheduling little social events on your social calendar. It could be drinks out with friends or even just a weekly Facetime with your sister or mom. Solitude is great, and I'm all for it, especially being an empath/HSP, but there's no substitute for interacting with people IRL. So don't be a vampire. Make time to squeeze in some socializing so you're not a complete hermit, living in a hole.

Home Magick

I love to incorporate magic in pretty much anything, especially my home. Since I'm such a little witch, my house has an absurd number of crystals (organized nicely on a white shelf) and protection symbols such as brooms hung up on walls and hanging on doorknobs. There's usually a crystal grid kicking around somewhere, and my dining room hutch is like a full blown apothecary with herbs I'm collecting in super cute jars. And of course, the most important magical place for me where I can connect with my desires, intentions, and goals in a spiritual way is my altar. My altar is where I can quiet the world, express gratitude, and connect with my inner power.

Make an Altar

Create a sacred space for your spirituality in your home. Self-care is also about engaging with your higher self, gods, deities, and the universe as well as working with your own energy and intentions. So why not give your spirituality a physical space in which to engage with it? No matter what your spiritual beliefs are, you can still benefit from creating an altar as a source of comfort. Altars are a beautiful way to creatively connect with your spiritual side, even if you're not into all that woo-woo. You can have entirely way too much fun choosing items and arranging them on your altar.

How to Create an Altar

Decide its purpose: Is it to make offerings, do rituals work, cast spells, etc.?
Pick a space: What spot in your home feels like the best place to have an altar?
Gather items: Collect any items or tools that resonate with you.
Have fun arranging items: Arrange your altar's items in the way most pleasing to you.
Enjoy the space: Enjoy and work within the space that serves your intentions.

You may put anything you wish on your altar. Here are some ideas:
- An offering bowl
- Antiques, bottles, photos
- Candles, crystals, decor
- Figurines of deities
- Incense and incense holders
- Keys, coins, jewelry
- Oils, potions, sprays
- Plants, flowers, herbs
- Symbolic or sentimental items

Create a Bathroom Sanctuary

Since water and bath time are such magical tools for self-care for empaths, why not create a super sacred bathroom sanctuary dedicated to all your awesome bath time? Romanticize your cleansing rituals as much as you want. Have fun with candles, crystals, oils, scents, herbs, aromas, bath bombs, salts—even make a bath time playlist for your bath wind-down time.

- Arrange some candles and crystals around the tub or use some eucalyptus spray in the shower.
- Choose items or decor that create a tranquil environment for you.
- Have an assortment of herbs, oils, essential oils, or aromas.
- Keep an arrangement of bath bombs or bath salts in a beautiful jar or container.
- Keep some bath spell kits nearby. (They can have a candle, a crystal, or some bath salts with herbs in them, or a magical bath bomb.)
- Place some plants on a shelf or on a ledge or counter.
- Set up a speaker to play a relaxing music playlist for your bath time.
- Stock up on some luxurious bath soaps and bubble bath.

Cleansing Your Home

Over time, energy accumulates in our home. Whether we ourselves have been stressed or overworked, or if we just threw a party or had guests over. Keep some sage bundles nearby or use incense to cleanse out the previous or negative energies in your home. Having some things to burn or cleansing sprays on hand is a wonderful way to reset a room for a highly sensitive person. I like to cleanse with smoke or sprays daily, as a way to completely reset the day. I especially like to spray something around my work area before I sit down to write so that it feels like a clean slate and a fresh start every time. Cleaning your home can become a self-care ritual as well. Though most of us view cleaning as a chore (it is), there *is* a way to turn home cleaning into a meditative, therapeutic act of self-love when you treat your environment as an extension of you. Cleansing your home in all ways is crucial to you feeling relaxed in your own space.

A TOOLBOX FOR
THE CREATIVE HOME

Do a home audit.

Spring clean: Ditch, donate, or sell.

Declutter and get organized.

Express yourself with decor.

Create a home office.

Create an end-of-day routine.

Try making an altar or bathroom sanctuary.

Self-Care for the Creative Home Workbook

Describe Your Personal Home Style

How would you describe your personal style when it comes to home decor? Are you more drawn to modern styles? Rustic chic? Glam and glitz? Antiques and oddities? What colors are you drawn to with your home style? Pops of bold colors? Or more neutral earthy colors? Write down a few sentences that describe your personal style for home decor. Include style, colors, and items that you are drawn to.

_____

_____

_____

_____

_____

_____

_____

_____

_____

Set Your Intentions with Your Space(s)

Just like you did with the home audit, walk around to each room and ask yourself what your intentions with each space are. What happens in each area, what's its use/purpose? What activities go on in this area? How do you want to *feel* in this area of your home?

Bedroom

What is the purpose of this room? What activities happen here?

_____

_____

_____

_____

_____

_____

My intention with this space:

_____

_____

_____

_____

_____

_____

The items I need in here to serve this purpose and intention are:

_____

_____

_____

_____

_____

_____

Bathroom

What is the purpose of this room? What activities happen here?

_____

_____

_____
_____
_____
_____

My intention with this space:

_____
_____
_____
_____
_____
_____

The items I need in here to serve this purpose and intention are:

_____
_____
_____
_____
_____

Kitchen

What is the purpose of this room? What activities happen here?

_____
_____
_____
_____
_____
_____

My intention with this space:

_____

_____

_____

_____

_____

_____

The items I need in here to serve this purpose and intention are:

_____

_____

_____

_____

_____

_____

Living Room

What is the purpose of this room? What activities happen here?

_____

_____

_____

_____

_____

My intention with this space:

_____

_____

_____

_____

_____

_____

The items I need in here to serve this purpose and intention are:

_____

_____

_____

_____

_____

_____

Work Area

What is the purpose of this room? What activities happen here?

_____

_____

_____

_____

_____

_____

My intention with this space:

_____

_____

_____

_____

_____

_____

The items I need in here to serve this purpose and intention are:

_____

_____

_____

_____

_____

_____

Closets

What is the purpose of this room? What activities happen here?

_____

_____

_____

_____

_____

_____

My intention with this space:

_____

_____

_____

_____

_____

_____

The items I need in here to serve this purpose and intention are:

_____

_____

_____

_____

_____

_____

Home Improvements

Walk through your home audit and your intention setting exercises and review your answers. Whatever the changes/solutions you came up with, it's worth spending time, effort, and/or money to give your space an overhaul, especially when your home is also your workspace. Make yourself a cute lil' shopping list.

What items do you need in your work/home office space to help you feel inspired?

What will help the closet spaces feel more organized and pleasing to look at?

What would make your sleep area more primed for a good night's sleep?

What would make your living room more relaxing? Some new candles or plants?

What will make your bathroom feel a little more like an oasis for self-care?

What items would make cooking more enjoyable for you in your kitchen?

Do you need additional furniture or shelving units to serve more purposes?

My home shopping list:

_____

_____

_____

_____

_____

_____

_____

_____

_____

_____

_____

_____

Assignment:

Go on an artist date to browse around stores and explore your personal style. Go to furniture stores, home decor shops, anywhere where you can feel inspired by items for your home. Check out Instagram, Tiktok, YouTube, Pinterest, or flip through some home decor magazines. Make a collage or mood board with the home decor style you'd wish to see within your home. Do a mood board for each room if you wish. Create a visual of the decor that best expresses who you are.

Home Maintenance

What do you want your home cleansing rituals to be like? Do a quick tidy up fifteen minutes a day? Spend an hour or two on the weekends cleaning up your home with some wine and a podcast? How do you envision cleansing your home in a way that's best with your schedule and provides you with a little more joy in cleaning? Or is it time to hire a cleaner once a week?

_____

_____

_____

_____

_____

CHAPTER SIX

Magical Self-Care

Witchcraft

These days, witchcraft is exploding into mainstream culture. And I'm totally here for it. While it's been around for thousands of years and present throughout history in many cultures, it's only in the past few decades that it's become popularized, considered more known, and accepted into society. Yet it's still completely loaded with stigma and misunderstood. Witchcraft is all about connecting to your personal power, tapping into your intuition, and directing your energy to create a desired outcome. It's also used for healing, ancestral connection, and receiving messages from the universe or your guides. It's an alternative way to connect with your spirituality if you don't necessarily believe in a particular religion.

To me, my practice with witchcraft is no different than using the law of attraction. You are using your own vibrational energy to create the life that you want by tapping into your higher self and source energy from the universe. Witchcraft is a highly creative way to get in touch with your spirituality, set your intentions, and create manifestations.

You also don't have to identify as a "witch" to participate in witchcraft. You can absolutely stir a little intention into your next cup of lavender-hibiscus tea. Pull an oracle card to receive guidance on the day. Or offer a bouquet of flowers on your dresser to express gratitude for all you have. Also, if you do identify as a witch, that doesn't necessarily mean that you follow the religion of Wicca or identify as Pagan either. There are no rules. Except for the ones you make! You get to participate in the world of magic without subscribing to a religion or putting titles on yourself such as a "witch" if you don't want to. For the record, I am 100 percent that witch.

In witchcraft rituals, nature is usually center stage. Whether you work with herbs or crystals or incorporate the earth's four elements of earth, air, fire, and water, you get to decide what objects or rituals hold meaning for you and what magical tools to work with. As empaths and highly sensitive people, working with various energies comes naturally to you. So witchcraft is actually the *perfect* outlet for an empath or HSP.

New Moon Rituals

The moon's cycle is completely embedded in the culture of witchcraft. The moon is responsible for the gravitational pull on the earth and controls the oceans' tides. As humans who are up to 60 percent water, the moon (whether you believe it or not) has an energetic effect on your body. Witches often base their rituals and spell work around the moon's cycle as each moon phase carries a different energy. Spell work can interact with it based on the intentions or purpose. Again, you don't have to call it "witchcraft" to participate in a new moon ritual if that doesn't resonate with you. You can absolutely reap the benefits of setting intentions a couple times a month as a way to check in with yourself, no labels attached.

New moon rituals are best for setting your intentions and thinking about what you want to call into your life. Think of it as a time to plant the seeds of the things that you wish to grow. It's a potent time to do manifestation spells and reflect on your goals and desires and whatever it is that you'd like to attract. New moons symbolize new beginnings, new projects, or a fresh start. You can create a new moon ritual based on your intention in whichever way resonates with you the most.

For example, if your new moon's intention is to bring more money into your life, a simple ritual to represent that could be to buy a plant or herb that has magical properties (such as mint, basil, or bamboo) and surround the plant with dollar bills. Close your eyes and connect with the *feeling* of flow and abundance. Seeing the plant will remind you of your intention and help you to vibrationally stay connected to that desire. Using whatever materials speak to you, here's a basic step by step on how to conduct a new moon ritual. But remember, you make the rules and you get to be as creative and elaborate as you want.

How to Do a New Moon Ritual

- Center and ground yourself.
- Cleanse your ritual space.
- Gather the necessary supplies.
- Light a candle.
- Meditate on your intention.

- Perform a ritual or spell with the chosen items.
- Write down your intentions on a piece of paper.

More Ideas for New Moon Rituals

- Create affirmations.
- Plant some seeds–literally. Set an intention.
- Pull an oracle or tarot card.
- Use herb medleys or incense that align with your intentions.
- Use magical products like soaps, body oils, potions, room sprays.
- Visualize what you want or make a vision board.

Full Moon Rituals

Full moons are great for releasing that which no longer serves you, and/or celebrating! They symbolize a cycle's full completion, abundance, and transformation, and it begins to shift into a waning energy, which means it's a time to let go, relax, and release. Use a full moon to celebrate any wins that you've had, to reflect on the last moon cycle, or to release anything that's not working for you. Full moons are a powerful time to let go and release fears, self-limiting beliefs, toxic energies, and anything that does not serve a purpose in your life.

How to Do a Full Moon Ritual

- Center and ground yourself.
- Cleanse your ritual space.

- Gather the necessary supplies.
- Light a candle.
- Meditate on what fears and self-limiting beliefs you wish to let go of.
- Meditate on your wins and celebrations.
- Perform a ritual or spell with the chosen items to symbolize the release.
- Write down what you're releasing or letting go of on a piece of paper. (Burn it if you wish!)

More Ideas for Full Moon Rituals

- Charge your crystals in the moonlight.
- Make moon water (water that has spent time under the light of a full moon).
- Pull an oracle or tarot card.
- Use herb medleys or incense.
- Use magical products like soaps, oils, sprays.
- Watch the moon.
- Write down what you're releasing/letting go of, then do a burning ritual.

Astrology 101

Astrology and our place in the cosmos plays a huge role in witchcraft. It literally means "wisdom of the stars." Tapping into the moon and planets and astrological events can help you plan for the future, make intuitive decisions based on your under-standing of your current circumstances, and set intentions for the path forward. Again, you can still play with astrology without all the witchy-ness and be super into mathematical degrees and positions of the planets.

Chances are you probably already know your astrological sign and some of the characteristics or traits that sign is best known for. For example, I'm a Capricorn: hard-working, goal oriented, stubborn, and a goat who climbs mountains for a living. These are all hard facts. The next level of astrology in getting to know yourself a tiny bit more is knowing your sun, moon, and rising signs. Finding your sun, moon, and rising is as easy as seeking a chart generator online and entering the time, date, and location you were born.

Sun Sign - The sun sign represents your drive, motivations, and/or ego.

Moon Sign - The moon sign represents our inner emotional world and who we are on a deeper soul level.

Rising Sign - The rising sign speaks to the type of energy that we put out into the world.

Knowing these three astrological signs may help you to better understand layers of yourself and spell out more to your identity than you realize. If you're finding knowing these facts about you helpful, maybe even get crazy with it and try dissecting your birth chart!

Crystal Healing

Crystals have been used for their spiritual, emotional, and healing properties for thousands of years. They've been worn as talismans, used in spells and rituals, placed on altars and in homes as decor, even used in the death masks of the kings and pharaohs of ancient Egypt. Basically, rocks form in the ground under a certain amount of pressure and the crystals themselves become infused with powerful energy stored within them.

Essentially, crystals can become your little energy buddies. I am the person who will grab a seat at the bar, order a beer, and pull out four crystals from my fanny pack to keep me company. This witch travels with crystals *everywhere* she goes. No shame. To me, they are quite literally my emotional support rocks.

How to Use Crystals

- Decorate your home or work desk with them.
- Hold them or meditate with them.
- Make a crystal grid (a formation of crystals used to set an intention).
- Place them on your altar.
- Plant them in your plants.
- Put them in your purse and carry them with you.
- Use them in spells and rituals.
- Use them in the bath.
- Wear them as a talisman or jewelry.

Types of Crystals and Their Benefits

There are a gazillion different types of crystals and rock specimens that come from all over the world that have all kinds of purposes. Here are some of the more common crystals and their meanings, benefits, and typical uses. Don't forget to research the type of crystal you're getting and the proper way to cleanse or care for your crystals as some need extra special care and shouldn't be run under water. If you're feeling drawn to a particular crystal, feel free to use that crystal for your own intentions, regardless of its description. When something's calling to you, lean into your own intuition!

Crystals	Benefits/Uses
AMAZONITE	Has a soothing effect on the nervous system. Associated with heart and throat chakra. Great stone for connecting with your heart. Inspires joy, confidence, hopefulness, effective communication, and self-expression.
AMETHYST	Associated with the crown and third eye chakra. A stone for tapping into your intuition and spirituality. Helps to calm the mind, balance emotions, battle addictions, make decisions, and activate courage. Helps with headaches/migraines, immunity boost, and deeper sleep.
AVENTURINE	A stone of prosperity, healing, abundance, and growth. Associated with the heart chakra, promotes compassion and empathy for yourself and others. Also used for calmness, career success, balance, and drawing in money.
BLACK TOURMALINE	A stone of protection that is used for warding off negative energy. Great for grounding and achieving a sense of balance. Transforms anxious and negative emotions. Associated with the base chakras, which helps you to feel safe and secure.
BLACK OBSIDIAN	Shields you from negative energies. Removes and absorbs negativity from an environment. Used for protection, purification, transformation, or dissolving emotional blocks. Also used for grounding.

Crystals	*Benefits/Uses*
CARNELIAN	Associated with the sacral chakra. Excellent stone for creativity and sexuality. Boosts your energy, motivation, and self-esteem. Great for stimulating creative ideas, increasing passion, courage, and empowerment.
CLEAR QUARTZ	A powerful amplifying stone. Used for purification, enhancing and channeling mental clarity, and strengthening the effects of other crystals. Associated with all chakras. Also used for manifestation and improving focus.
FLUORITE	Used for flushing out toxic energies, improving your immune system and overall health, and getting over a cold/flu or illness. A great healing stone. Clears mind of distractions, helps with learning and making decisions.
JADE	Associated with wealth, abundance, and prosperity. Creates harmony of the mind, body, and spirit. Considered a stone of "good luck" and good fortune. Also contains soothing and calming properties. Helps the heart to make the right decisions and to balance emotions.
ROSE QUARTZ	A powerful love stone. Can be used to attract love and friendships, as well being a stone of self-love and self-compassion. It activates and aligns the heart chakra, and it is said to be the stone of unconditional love. Heals emotional wounds.
SMOKY QUARTZ	A powerful grounding stone that has shielding properties. Can be used to transmute or transform negative energies. Brings emotional calmness, relieves stress and anxiety, disperses fear, and helps to lift depression.

Crystals	*Benefits/Uses*
SODALITE	Associated with the third eye-chakra. It encourages truth, supports intuition, and communication. Said to be the "poet's stone." Helps to overcome negative thinking, boosts mental clarity and self-confidence.

Crystal Grids

A couple years back, I was experiencing really bad insomnia and decided to try my hand at making a crystal grid. I found one with hematite and howlite stones placed in a circle shape, sprinkled with relaxing lavender all around it. Its presence on my dresser helped me find a sense of calm and relief and reminded me of my desire for a restful sleep. The result? I slept like a baby.

You can harness the powers of crystals by setting an intention with a crystal grid. You can create a crystal grid by combining various crystals and incorporating natural elements like dried herbs, flowers, or plants. Crystal grids use geometric patterns to amplify the energetic powers of the items in your grid and remind you of your intention by placing it somewhere where you can see it and receive the visual reminder of it. Crystal grids are not only stunning to look at but can be used for any intention, such as road openers, heart openers, attracting money, abundance, prosperity—whatever your little heart desires.

A Sleep Crystal Grid

Here is the crystal grid that helped me out of my insomnia moment and into a restful sleep.

For this crystal grid, you will need:

A focus piece clear quartz tower or cluster
Four pieces of tumbled howlite

Four pieces of tumbled hematite
Lavender

Directions:

Place your focus piece clear quartz crystal in the center.
Place your four hematite and four howlite in a circle, around the clear quartz, alternating and equidistant.
Decorate the in-between spaces with lavender.

How to Make a Crystal Grid

- Think of your intention.
- Note any crystals that serve this purpose.
- Collect any other items you'd like to include.
- Explore a geometric shape that you'd like to set up as a layout.
- Choose the ideal spot to place the grid.
- Position the items in an arrangement that's pleasing to you.
- Energetically activate the grid. (Tap the crystals, or close your eyes and place your hands over it to activate the grid.)
- Leave it there (untouched) for as long you think you need it.

Spellcasting

Here's a funny story of how I cast an epic spell before I was consciously aware that I was a witch. Recovering from my narc trauma was like an emotional tsunami. My healing process included waves of grief and being swept away by the undertow of the effects of narc abuse. Leaning into my spiritual side became my only means of coping. My house was beginning to look like an apothecary, and I'd been going to crystal stores on the regular to find some inner soothing. Each crystal became like a little Band-Aid to my heart. I realized I needed to *DO* something to represent and honor my decision to cut this person out of my life. I needed to grieve the loss of this person, and I wanted to put my own positive spin on the whole experience. So I conjured up a full-blown ritual to symbolize and honor my decision and celebrate a new commitment of self-love to myself.

My ritual was a whole-day affair that I held in my backyard next to my fruit trees in the sunshine. I put on a white dress and carried a bouquet of flowers down the lawn to symbolize a "wedding" where I made new vows and commitments to myself. Then, I wrote a letter to this person and did a "burning" over a bonfire, allowing the smoke to transmute all the pain and anger. Next, I held a "funeral" where I could fully grieve the loss of this person, bury some old photos in the ground, and say my final good-byes. To finish it off, I did a cord-cutting ritual by burning two candles wrapped in twine. This super-extra series of events was a gigantic act of self-love that helped me to affirm my decision to be brave enough to walk away and never look back.

This day was so incredibly powerful for me because it gave my mind, body, and spirit a chance to physically and emotionally burn the past, say yes to a more loving future for myself, and let go of what wasn't serving me. Because of this ritual, I was able to fully walk away from the toxic relationship I'd been experiencing. It wasn't until shortly after this ceremony that it hit me like a ton of bricks and I said, "Holy shit, I'm a fucking witch."

Even though I didn't know it at the time, I mark this day and the performance of this ritual as the day I became a witch. I'd come to magic naturally all on my own as a way to find solace, comfort, and healing. As a way to shift my energy and manifest something entirely new. And it *worked*. This is what magic is ALL about.

Types of Spells

A spell is anything infused with your energy and intention. It could be in the form of tea, candles, jewelry, spell jars, charms, potions, oils, crystal grids, mojo bags, rituals, or even cooking and infusing your food with intention. There are endless ways to do a spell. Spellcasting is the art of raising and directing your energy. How you want to craft a ritual based on your intentions is all up to you. Spells can incorporate *anything*. Use herbs, plants, flowers, crystals, salts, little figurines, coins, stones, whatever has sentimental value or represents or symbolizes your intention. The best part? You get to tap into your heart's desires, use your imagination (and your energy), and be as creative as you want to be in conducting your spells! Here are some basic spells you can try out.

Protection Spells	
Crystals you may use	Black obsidian, black tourmaline, pyrite, shungite, onyx, and smoky quartz are great stones that have protective, shielding, and grounding qualities.
Candles	Black
Herbs	Garlic, rosemary, lavender, juniper, black salts
Sprays	Rosemary sprays
Protection Spell	Cleanse and arrange materials. Cast a circle with salt. Light black candle. Center and ground yourself. Meditate and ask guides for protection. Make an offering such as flowers or fruit as gratitude to the universe or your guides. Spray self with protective spray. Wear or carry a protective stone with you.

Money Spells	
Crystals you may use	Green aventurine, jade, citrine, tiger's eye, pyrite, and moss agate are great money drawing, abundance, and prosperity stones.
Candles	Green
Herbs	Bay leaf, ginger, basil, mint, cloves, thyme, jasmine, lemongrass, cinnamon
Money Spells	Carry a bay leaf in your wallet. Write an amount of money on the bay leaf and burn it. Create a money altar around a plant (basil, mint, and bamboo are great wealth attractors). Collect dollar bills, coins, and checks and arrange them around the plant to signify the flow of cash. Place crystals of your choice on the cash to amplify its energy.

Friendship spell	
Crystals you may use	Lapis, clear quartz, rose quartz, amethyst, peridot, moss agate, and yellow topaz
Materials	Flowers, herbs, crystals, salts, spell jar
Candles	Yellow or pink
Herbs	Yellow rose petals, catnip, lavender, sunflower, geranium
Friendship spell	Cleanse crystals and spell jar. Meditate and visualize the friendship you'd like to attract. Arrange a combination of flowers, herbs, crystals, and salts into your spell jar. (Example: lapis and rose quartz crystals, lavender, sunflower, pink Himalayan salts, and rose petals.) Place the top cork on the spell jar and seal it with melted wax from a pink or yellow candle.

Self-Love Spells	
Crystals you may use	Rose quartz, amethyst, clear quartz, and pink amethyst
Candles	Pink
Herbs	Roses, rose buds, lavender, chamomile, lemon balm
Self-love spell	Draw a self-love bath. Add some bath salts. Add lavender, rose buds, or rose petals. Light a pink candle. Surround the tub with crystals of your choice. Relax and enjoy a soothing bath. Say positive affirmations to yourself.

Cord Cutting Spells	
Crystals you may use	Black obsidian, black tourmaline, pyrite, shungite, onyx, and smoky quartz are great protective, shielding, and grounding stones. Since cord cutting is emotionally tough, you may want to add some rose quartz, clear quartz, or amethyst to add some self-love, clarity, and third eye insights.
Materials	One white candle, one black candle, twine, small knife to carve
Cord-cutting spell	Cleanse and arrange all materials. Take the knife and carve the person's name into the black candle. Carve your name into the white candle. On the plate, burn the bottoms of the candles so you can stick each candle evenly on the melted wax to have both candles stand next to each other. Take the twine and wrap it a couple times around both candles and tie a bow. Light both candles at the same time. Let the candles burn down and cut the cord by burning the twine. Write your intentions, reflect, journal.

Road Opener Spells	
Crystals you may use	Carnelian, citrine, tiger's eye, pyrite, aventurine, clear quartz, selenite, sodalite, and bumblebee jasper
Materials	Keys, road opener oils, and sprays
Candles	Orange, white, or a multi-color candle
Herbs	Bay leaf, garlic, lemon balm, mint, parsley, rosehip, rosemary, valerian, verbena
Road opener spell	Cleanse and arrange all materials. Set up two rows of chime candles, creating a "pathway" or "road" formation. Outline the path with crystals of your choice. At the end of the "path," place an object that symbolizes the thing you wish to arrive at. It could be a money tree, an object to represent an opportunity, or simply some words written on a paper. Light the candles. Center and ground yourself. While holding a key, write down any blockages you are willing to release, then meditate on your desired outcome. Wear or carry the key with you.

Divination: Tarot and Oracle Cards

Divination is a *wonderful* way for empaths and HSPs to play with their sensitivity and consult their own guides. Even if you don't believe in all that woo-woo, divination has actually been part of many different cultures and existed in ancient civilizations. Did you know some therapists have even started to use the visual aspects of tarot cards to help their clients grasp a deeper understanding of their own mental and emotional experiences and what their intuition is telling them? Divination can be a *powerful* solo practice with just yourself. You don't have to know the history of the cards or the meanings of the cards to benefit from their use. In fact, learning about them in the process is part of the fun! Interpreting the cards in itself is a super artistic and creative way to explore our visceral reactions to the images. It can provide a way for you to consult your own intuition and gut feelings towards your life, help you to interpret your current situation or the problems you're facing, and connect with your own higher self through interpreting the visuals of the cards.

What the Hell Are Chakras, Anyway?

The chakra system originated in India sometime between 1500 and 500 BC. Chakra in Sanskrit means "wheel" and it refers to the seven different energy points in the body. They correspond with different nerves and organs as well as the energetic body. If there are any blockages, they can affect us emotionally and mentally. Chakras are particularly helpful to know and understand if you are experiencing different sensations throughout the body. If you have a sore throat, your throat chakra may be blocked. If you're feeling particularly sassy lately, maybe your sacral chakra is wide open. I've personally experienced panic attacks in my stomach, or the "solar plexus," which can be referred to as the place responsible for confidence, self-esteem, and feeling in control of your life. I like to think of chakras as my body's alert system. If there's a physical sensation I'm feeling, that's my cue to investigate what else could be going on with me internally (emotionally, mentally, spiritually). Here's a snapshot of the chakras, their meanings, and how they align with certain crystals and essential oils.

CHAKRA	*MEANING*	*OILS*	*CRYSTALS*
CROWN	Divine wisdom, universal consciousness, bliss, enlightenment	Rose, lavender, frankincense, jasmine, myrrh	Clear quartz, selenite, amethyst, howlite, sugalite
THIRD EYE	Intuition, manifestation, clairvoyance, imagination projection of will, peace of mind	Mint, mugwort, lavender, star anise, rosemary	Lapis lazuli, azurite, calcite, kyanite, fluorite, sodalite
THROAT	Self-expression, communication, freedom, inspiration, truth, independence	Sage, eucalyptus, bergamot, chamomile, tea tree	Turquoise, amazonite, aquamarine, blue lace agate, chalcedony, chrysocolla, apatite
HEART	Unconditional love, healing, harmony, compassion, transformation, sharing	Lavender, lemon, wild orange, rose geranium, ylang-ylang	Jade, aventurine, rose quartz, malachite, tourmaline, kunzite
SOLAR PLEXUS	Personal power, self-control, peace, self-acceptance, identity, inner harmony, authority, joy	Grapefruit, cinnamon, cypress, clove, coriander	Citrine, calcite, tiger's eye, yellow agate, light amber

CHAKRA	MEANING	OILS	CRYSTALS
SACRAL	Sexuality, creativity, pleasure, primal instinct, desire, openness, personal creativity	Neroli, patchouli, sandalwood, ylang-ylang, gardenia	Carnelian, moonstone, gold calcite, dark amber, yellow jasper
ROOT	Stability, survival, grounding, courage, trust, full acceptance of life, will power to achieve goals, satisfaction, vitality	Sandalwood, cedarwood, frankincense, patchouli, black pepper	Obsidian, red jasper, agate, bloodstone, hematite

A TOOLBOX FOR
MAGICAL SELF-CARE

Try new moon rituals.

Try full moon rituals.

Learn about your sun, moon, and rising sign.

Use crystals or crystal grids.

Try spellcasting for any intention.

Use tarot or oracle cards to tap into your intuition.

Utilize the chakra system for self-care.

Magical Self-Care Workbook

Here are some magical self-care prompts to help you get in touch with your intuition, desires, and personal power. You may even find it helpful to keep a magical journal to write down any spells, intentions, or intuitions you may have throughout moon cycles.

Things I Find Magical Are:

List anything that you find to be magical and inspiring, consider to be signs from the universe, or things that make you feel connected to divine source energy. (For example, it could be angel numbers, tarot cards, deities, sigils, animals, nature—anything you have a spiritual connection with.)

_____

_____

_____

_____

_____

_____

_____

_____

_____

_____

_____

_____

_____

_____

_____

_____

Rituals that Are Important in My Culture:

Are there any rituals or traditions that are important in your life? Are there any rituals you feel a calling to explore or learn more about? List anything from your culture or curiosities that you find to have significant meaning or importance to you.

_____

_____

_____

_____

_____

_____

_____

_____

_____

_____

_____

_____

_____

_____

_____

Magical Exercises:

- Incorporate objects that feel magical and/or special to you in a ritual.
- Incorporate something meaningful from your culture in a ritual.
- Learn about your astrological birth chart.
- Note any crystals or stones that you are drawn to and

notice how you feel when you hold them.

- Note any plants, herbs, or objects that you feel a connection with.
- Note anything spiritual that you are particularly curious about.
- Pull a tarot/oracle card and spend time journaling about it.
- Spend time learning about any figures, deities, or gods that resonate with you.
- Start a new moon and full moon journal to set your intentions and do your rituals.

Crafting a Spell

Anyone can craft a spell. While there are thousands of spells you can try, coming up with your own spell is exactly what makes it personal, fun, and tailored to you and your energy. Here's how to create your own spell with any intention.

Start with choosing an intention.

My intention is:

_____
_____
_____
_____
_____
_____

Example: My intention is to draw in more money, attract new friends, manifest good health, etc.

Identify things or items that represent your intention.

Things that represent this intention are:

_____

_____

_____

_____

_____

_____

Example: cash money, a friendship bracelet, a beautiful plant, etc.

Decide on a ritual or activity to call in your intention that includes these items.

A ritual or activity that symbolizes my intention is:

_____

_____

_____

_____

_____

_____

Example: Place dollar bills all around a basil plant, write a letter to your ideal new best friend and wear a friendship bracelet, or take a walk in nature and imagine good health by breathing in the fresh air.

Ta da! You just did a Nina Simone and put a spell on me. Spell work can be as simple and easy as that. It doesn't have to be complicated, *but* you get to decide how elaborate and in-depth you want to take it. Fun, right?

CHAPTER SEVEN

Design Your Self-Care Toolkit

Congratulations on being awesome! You've done some incredibly brave and courageous work already to get to this point, and you should definitely take a pause and celebrate the fact that you've decided to put this much time, care, and attention into yourself already. Clap hands emoji.

For our final time together, we are going to build you a self-care toolkit for you to turn to whenever the life shitstorm decides to hit, and you need a plan of action so that you never have to feel stuck, stranded, or lost ever again. We're gonna do this in a fun, prepper way. Where we think through all the possible worst-case scenarios and build you a proper plan for them. Even though you can't plan for everything in life, having this toolkit with you at all times is going to make it that much easier for you to recover from any scenario.

I'm going to guide you through this, but we are tailoring something specific *for you,* so fill in the blanks according to you so that this thing has your fingerprint on it; it's your self-care plan made just for you.

DESIGN YOUR SELF-CARE
TOOLKIT WORKBOOK

Let's start by filling in these boxes with all the things you find pleasure in, raise your energetic vibration, or simply make you happy. These lists are going to be your go-tos in a pinch—and the things that can motivate you to get awesome work done.

Pleasure Bundle List

Write down all the activities that bring you pleasure and joy and make you happy.

_____

_____

_____

_____

_____

_____

_____

_____

_____

_____

_____

_____

_____

_____

_____

_____

_____

_____

High Vibe List

Write down all the activities and things that raise your energetic vibration.

_____

_____

_____

_____

_____
_____
_____
_____
_____
_____
_____
_____
_____
_____
_____
_____
_____
_____
_____

Happys

Write down all the things that would make you happy if you were temporarily feeling bummed or sad.

_____
_____
_____
_____
_____
_____
_____
_____
_____
_____
_____

_____
_____
_____
_____
_____
_____

Nurturing to Your Creativity

Write down all the things that nurture your creativity, make you feel inspired, or make your inner child feel comforted, curious, or playful. (Like Artist Dates, for example.)

_____
_____
_____
_____
_____
_____
_____
_____
_____
_____
_____
_____
_____
_____
_____
_____
_____

Self-Care Categories

Of the pleasure bundle, high vibe, and happy lists, pull out each of the items and assign them the category that they best serve. You may repeat the same item multiple times in each category. These are your personal favorite go-to strategies so that if any of these areas of your life seem to take a dip in any way, you have an immediate action you can take to give you a bump. Fill in each of these spaces and put anything else you find helpful for you. Add any additional spaces as you see fit! Include more items if they come up.

Mental Self-Care

_____
_____
_____
_____
_____
_____
_____
_____
_____
_____
_____
_____
_____
_____
_____
_____
_____

Physical Self-Care

_____
_____
_____
_____
_____
_____
_____
_____
_____
_____
_____
_____
_____
_____
_____
_____
_____
_____
_____
_____
_____
_____
_____
_____
_____
_____

Emotional Self-Care

_____

_____

_____

_____

_____

_____

_____

_____

_____

_____

_____

_____

_____

_____

_____

_____

_____

_____

_____

_____

_____

_____

_____

_____

_____

_____

_____

_____

Spiritual Self-Care

Social Self-Care

_____
_____
_____
_____
_____
_____
_____
_____
_____
_____
_____
_____
_____
_____
_____
_____
_____
_____
_____
_____
_____
_____
_____
_____
_____
_____
_____
_____

Vocational Self-Care

_____
_____
_____
_____
_____
_____
_____
_____
_____
_____
_____
_____
_____
_____
_____
_____
_____
_____
_____
_____
_____
_____
_____
_____
_____
_____

Sexual Self-Care

_____

_____

_____

_____

_____

_____

_____

_____

_____

_____

_____

_____

_____

_____

_____

_____

_____

_____

_____

_____

_____

_____

_____

_____

_____

_____

Feel free to add more of your own self-care categories here if you wish . . .

_____

_____

_____

_____

_____

_____

_____

_____

_____

_____

_____

_____

_____

_____

_____

_____

_____

_____

_____

_____

_____

_____

_____

_____

Daily Case Scenarios

Cool. Now that you have a list of all your favorite things in the world and a bucket of things that make you happy, raise your vibration, or help you in some way, AND you've categorized them into areas of self-care so you can call on them on the drop of a dime, let's come up with a self-care plan for some daily case scenarios so that you always have a go-to no matter what. Fill in the sentences below with all the things that would best help you through the daily case scenario. You don't have to know an answer for everything and you don't need to have anything super complicated in there either. Just write whatever comes to mind that you would find helpful in that scenario.

What to Do When . . .

I've had a stressful day.

_____

_____

_____

_____

_____

_____

I'm feeling burnt out.

_____

_____

_____
_____
_____
_____

I'm feeling tired and exhausted.

_____
_____
_____
_____
_____
_____

I've had a tough conversation with a coworker, friend, or relative.

_____
_____
_____
_____
_____

I've experienced a disappointment.

_____
_____
_____
_____

_____

_____

I'm feeling angry, sad, or emotional.

_____

_____

_____

_____

_____

_____

I experience physical pain in my body.

_____

_____

_____

_____

_____

I feel overstimulated in a hectic environment.

_____

_____

_____

_____

_____

_____

I'm feeling a mixed bag of emotions.

_____

_____

_____

_____

_____

_____

I feel like someone's crossed a boundary.

_____

_____

_____

_____

_____

_____

I feel overwhelmed with all of life's to-dos.

_____

_____

_____

_____

_____

_____

I feel creatively stuck.

_____

_____

_____

_____

_____

_____

I feel uninspired.

_____

_____

_____

_____

_____

_____

I'm feeling discouraged.

_____

_____

_____

_____

_____

_____

I fell down a social media doom scroll.

_____
_____
_____
_____
_____
_____

I'm feeling envious or jealous of others' success.

_____
_____
_____
_____
_____
_____

I'm feeling down about myself.

_____
_____
_____
_____
_____
_____

I'm experiencing anxiety.

_____

_____

_____

_____

_____

_____

I'm having a panic attack.

_____

_____

_____

_____

_____

_____

I'm feeling lost or hopeless about a difficult situation.

_____

_____

_____

_____

_____

_____

I'm experiencing depression.

_____

_____

_____

_____

_____

_____

I'm dealing with a self-limiting belief.

_____

_____

_____

_____

_____

_____

Feel free to add a few more scenarios of your choice here. Write down any potential potholes you see in your life's path—things that have occurred in the past or are likely to occur in the future. Anything that you may find stressful, write down that scenario and create a plan for it. What are some scenarios that may occur that you could develop a plan for?

_____

_____

_____

_____

_____

_____

_____

_____

_____

_____

_____

Methods and Techniques

Here are some of the methods and techniques in this book put to use in some of these scenarios.

When I'm feeling overwhelmed with emotions after a long day of socializing:

I will use the Emotion Separation technique.

When I am feeling uninspired or overwhelmed with my goals, ideas, or plans:

I will use strategies like Mind Mapping, Vision Boarding, or the Success Map from chapter four.

When I am feeling overwhelmed by all the to-dos and not having enough time:

I will time track and use the go-to time saver strategies in chapter four, such as Ditch or Delegate, to free up time and space.

When I'm experiencing writer's block or feeling uninspired:

I will plan some Artist Dates, start up my Morning Pages, or plan a Workation.

When I'm dealing with a gremlin or self-limiting belief:

I will use the technique Rewrite the Belief from chapter two.

When I am feeling unsure of which projects to take or what my next steps are:

I will pull up a mission statement and write down all the ideas that excite me and feel in line with my mission statement.

When I am feeling down about myself on social media:

I will activate my personal code of conduct towards social media and enforce my boundaries.

When I'm struggling with depression:

I will use the technique The Shortlist, drop back down to the basics of self-care and/or consider reaching out to a therapist for additional support.

Write out a few more scenarios in which you might be able to use the methods and techniques in this book.

_____

_____

_____

_____

Worst-Case Scenarios

Sometimes, we get hit with some worst-case scenarios and life can get really hard. When it's a worst-case scenario that can span over the course of weeks, months, years, you need a little different plan, geared for patience, self-compassion, and a whole lot of self-care over an extended period of time. Here are the four major worst-case scenarios that take time to process and will likely need multiple ongoing strategies until you feel a sense of healing, recovery, and wholeness. The big four are loss, grief, transition, and change.

What to Do When . . .

I Experience Loss:

- Talk to a therapist.
- Join a support group.
- Spend time processing my emotions through journaling or art.
- Express myself creatively.
- Do a cord-cutting ritual.
- Write a letter to this person and burn it.
- Create an altar to honor this person.
- Discuss my loss with friends and family.
- Drop down to the basics of self-care when I have a low capacity for much else.
- Spend time reading about loss and life after loss.
- Make something to commemorate or remember this person.

- Connect with my spirituality.
- Have patience with myself and self-compassion.

I Experience Grief:

- Talk to a therapist.
- Join a support group.
- Spend time processing my emotions through journaling or art.
- Express myself creatively.
- Discuss my grief with friends and family.
- Drop down to the basics of self-care when I have a low capacity for much else.
- Spend time reading about grief and the process of recovering from grief.
- Get enough rest.
- Hydrate and eat nutritious meals.
- Try a new hobby or a different artform.
- Connect with my spirituality.
- Have patience with myself and self-compassion.

I Go Through a Transition:

- Talk to a therapist.
- Journal my thoughts and feelings around this transition.
- Turn to my list of pleasure bundles, happys, and high vibration activities for comforts.
- Create a new routine that suits the needs of my transition.
- Discuss my transition with friends or family.
- Get enough rest.
- Get enough exercise.
- Connect with source and/or nature.

- Lean on relationships for extra support.
- Go on some Artist Dates.
- Decorate my home to suit my new needs.
- Cook some delicious meals for comfort.

I Go Through a Big Change:

- Talk to a therapist.
- Journal my thoughts and feelings around this change.
- Turn to my list of pleasure bundle, happys, and high vibration activities for comforts.
- Create a new routine that suits the needs of this change.
- Discuss this change with friends or family.
- Get enough rest.
- Hydrate and eat nutritious meals.
- Connect with source and/or nature.
- Lean on relationships for extra support.
- Go on some Artist Dates.
- Do a spell or ritual to commemorate or celebrate this new change.
- Cook some delicious meals for comfort.

Mental and Emotional Emergencies

If it's a mental or emotional emergency, never be ashamed to reach out for help. Reach out to your most trusted friends and family for support. See a list of help hotlines, professional therapists, organizations, resources, websites, and apps at the end of this book.

Self-Care Maintenance Plan

Now, let's get you going with a self-care maintenance plan that will keep you feeling solid at a base level, as well as keep you feeling sane, and able to handle life like a boss. This is the plan that you can keep in your back pocket as an ongoing staple in your life. If I'm a self-care doctor, this is your self-care prescription. In the box below, I want you to write down all the self-care pillars that you absolutely need to stay sane. Write down all the non-negotiables.

All the Non-Negotiables

_____

_____

_____

_____

_____

_____

_____

_____

_____

_____

_____

_____

_____

_____

Plan Your Self-Care Musts

Referring back to creating your routines in the previous chapters, schedule all of these non-negotiable self-care musts into the appropriate times so that you create space for all your self-care needs no matter what. Take your self-care activity and place it everywhere it fits. This way, when you're scheduling your time, you know exactly what your self-care priorities are and where to fit them.

Morning Routine

_____

_____

_____

_____

_____

_____

Evening Routine

_____

_____

_____

_____

_____

_____

End-of-Day Routine

_____

_____

_____

_____

_____

_____

Weekly Routine

_____

_____

_____

_____

_____

_____

Monthly Routine

_____

_____

_____

_____

_____

_____

Yearly Routine

_____

_____

_____

_____

_____

Create a Self-Care Visual

For your final exercise, create a self-care visual that represents all the self-care activities that bring you restoration, joy, comfort, soothing, nurturing, fun, and inspiration. Have fun drawing pictures and coloring it in and hang it somewhere where you can see it as a visual reminder that you always have something to call on whenever it's a self-care emergency.

The Send-Off

Wow! Look at all this amazing, incredible self-reflection you did in this workbook. This is kind of a big deal. A lot of people don't even bother stopping to take the time to ask themselves these important questions to truly take care of themselves, but you have. You should be proud. Before we part ways, know you can always come back here, redo this book again, and create a brand new self-care toolkit for yourself at any point, at any time. Thank you for spending this time with me. I'm so dang proud of you and I know you are going to do incredible things. I'd love to stay connected with you throughout your artist journey and offer a chance to come work with me more after this book. Join my community for VIP access to events, workshops, and check out the *Self-Care for the Creative* podcast for even more self-care gems! Let's stay in touch. And don't forget, support is always available to you. Self-care is always within reach, and your greatest masterpiece will always be *you*. You got this.

Love, Stefani

A Fireside Chat on Self-Care and the Creative Process

Bonnie McKee

(She/Her)
Singer, Songwriter, Actress, Screenwriter, Director

Bonnie McKee has written ten No. One hit songs with some of the biggest pop stars including Katy Perry, Britney Spears, Kesha, Kelly Clarkson, Jason Derulo, Christina Aguilera, Carly Rae Jepson, Bebe Rexha, and Cher. She's been nominated for a Grammy for "Song of the Year" for cowriting "Roar" with Katy Perry, which became a diamond certified record. Bonnie's single, "American Girl," has amassed over thirty-nine million streams and her EP *Bombastic* charted in the top ten on iTunes. She is also an award-winning actress, director, and screenwriter. Her short film called *April Kills the Vibe* won fifty-three film festival awards.

1. Introduce yourself. Tell us who you are and what you do. Give us an overview of your career so far. (If possible, include some career highs and lows.) Give us a brief description of what daily life looks like for you.

I miraculously signed a record deal and moved to LA by myself at sixteen years old. I started as an industry darling and was quickly discarded after my first album, *Trouble*, flopped. After several years of being broke and feeling like I was worthless, I started writing songs for other artists out of necessity, and a chance encounter with a young, undiscovered artist named Katy Perry changed my life. We were both selling our clothes at a thrift store and became fast friends, and she later invited me to write on her sophomore album, *Teenage Dream*. I signed a publishing deal and suddenly, very accidentally, became a hit songwriter.

For many years, my day-to-day was going into every studio in LA and many times traveling the world, working with different writers and producers, and writing a song a day and sometimes two or three. My heart was always in performing, however, so I signed another record deal and released my first single, "American Girl," which did fairly well, but paled in comparison to my prior global successes writing with other artists, which was of course difficult.

The day-to-day of being an artist consisted of photo shoots, video shoots, rehearsals, content creation, a lot of travel, and again writing and recording songs for my own project while simultaneously writing for my contemporaries. After disagreements with the label, I left. On my own again, I released my first independent EP, *Bombastic*, with surprising success. I thrived being independent and loved having complete creative freedom without a label breathing down my neck, but being independent is a full-time job in itself. It's difficult being your own boss, making your own deadlines, and having nobody to answer to.

As an ADD creative, staying motivated and on task can be extremely overwhelming and oftentimes emotional. That being said, I'm a scrappy DIY queen, so I spend a lot of time designing my own sets, making costumes, and editing my own vocals and videos, which I love. I learned about video budgets, social media strategy, and everything in between, which helped immensely when I decided to move into screenwriting and directing. These days I'm trying to learn more about time management so I can find the time to work on the many projects I want to create. Spoiler alert—haven't mastered that one yet.

2. Tell us about your creative process. What works best for you? Have you experienced writer's block, imposter syndrome, procrastination, perfectionism, self-doubt, or self-limiting beliefs? How did you overcome them?

I am absolutely a perfectionist to the point that I can become paralyzed and crippled with anxiety. I've definitely experienced writer's block, and it usually strikes when I've been "over writing." If I spend too much time in the studio, I can run out of things to write about because I have no life. It's imperative that I recharge my creative battery or I'm completely useless. I find that if I'm "on a roll" and write a crop of great songs in a row, I know the day will come when I sit down to write and nothing comes out. I used to punish myself and continue pushing until I was pulling my hair out, but I've found that if I hit a wall, it means I need a break. So I'll go to the movies, go out with friends, or even just sit still and stare at the wall for a few days or even weeks.

There was one point where I took nearly a year off because I got to a point where I'd sit down to write and just burst into tears. So rather than feeling like taking time off is "procrastinating" or "wasting time," I think of that as part of the process to get my best work. I need to be quiet and still to let the universe/aliens/angels or whoever it is that whispers in my ear to speak to me. If it's too loud or chaotic, I can't hear them.

As far as imposter syndrome, big yes. When everyone was congratulating and praising me for my success with Katy Perry, I felt like I didn't deserve it. I was in the room with the biggest producers (Max Martin and Doctor Luke) and literally the biggest pop star in the world; it would have been a hit with or without me, I thought. But after years of assessing my part in those songs (and a lot of therapy), I'm finally able to own the fact that I had a heavy hand in some groundbreaking art.

3. If comfortable sharing, tell us how you've previously struggled with your mental health. (Have you experienced anxiety, depression, a learning disability, ADHD, bipolar disorder? Or have you experienced adversity with your gender, sexuality, race?) What other challenges have you faced as a creative?

I am a recovering addict and alcoholic (eleven years sober!) and I've struggled with depression, anxiety, and ADD my whole life. Staying mentally healthy is a full-time job, and honestly the most important one. If my head isn't on straight, my art suffers, my relationships suffer. I used to buy into the tropes of being a "tortured artist" to excuse and justify my self-destructive behavior, but honestly once I had real opportunities on the line, I knew I had to make my mental health a priority. My mind is my moneymaker. I blew my first big opportunity when I got signed at sixteen, and after years of struggling in the industry, I knew that second chances are few and far between. Ultimately, success was more important to me than being a dark and twisty dumpster fire, so I chose a different path.

4. Tell us what you did (or continue to do) to cope with these challenges. Tell us some of the best strategies that have helped you overcome these struggles.

I take my meds, go to therapy, work out, work a twelve-step program, and read a lot of self-help books. I also practice a little witchy stuff just to keep things interesting. The type of "magic" I practice is really just elaborate affirmations and ritualized manifestation. Set an intention, write it down, read it out loud, light a candle, burn some incense, lie naked in the moonlight. Ya know, typical artist shit. It sounds stupid but I gotta say, it works. If not only because it's time set aside to be quiet and still and reflect. This business is one that requires a healthy dose of delusion, and being a realist can sometimes get me in trouble and hurl me into the swamp of sadness and self-doubt. On paper, the odds are against me, so if I'm living in a current reality where my dreams seem so out of reach, it's easy to get into "what's the point?" mode. But if I believe in magic, anything is possible.

5. Are there any other art forms, hobbies, or interests you engage in to help restore your creative energy? What nurtures your soul? Any creative activities that recharge you?

I'm definitely visually stimulated, so I'm passionate about interior design! I am deeply affected by my physical surroundings, and I find that a little color in my space can do wonders for me creatively. I'm so emotionally affected by color, I've been known to bring my own vibe lighting to a session if I know the studio is stark or has no "vibe." Haha!

Even when I was broke, if I was feeling down, I would spend my last dollar buying a can of colored paint to brighten things up or hang some Christmas lights to get a pop of color or tape up pretty pictures from magazines. I really think that having pretty things to look at, even if they're not expensive or fancy, can inspire me and get me daydreaming. Also watching artsy films or making mood boards opens a window into things I'm not exposed to in my day-to-day life, and that can conjure ideas I wouldn't have otherwise had.

6. What do you do for your self-care? Share any specific strategies, habits, or techniques that you find effective in improving your mental, emotional, physical, or spiritual self-care.

Hot baths. Unapologetic lazy days. Fancy food. Journaling. Yoga. Therapy. Twelve-step programs. Korean spa. I also find that, since my work is so much about stimulating my mind, it's refreshing to do things with my hands. Cooking, crafting, assembling furniture, shampooing the rug. There's something really meditative about working with my hands that gets me out of my head and into the moment.

7. What's one piece of self-care advice you would give to a person just starting out in a creative career?

Don't make success your higher power. Worshiping at the altar of success in the creative field means putting all of your self-worth into the opinions of others, and you have no control over what other people think. Learn to take constructive criticism and don't take it personally. Get your ten thousand hours in, hone your craft, do the work, but don't measure your personal value on whether or not you win. Hard as it is, try to separate your personal identity from your art. You're still valuable whether you make it or not. Stay away from toxic people. There are plenty of people to collaborate with and plenty of people who can give you opportunities, so don't tolerate shitty people just because you think they're your only way in. And finally, remember to enjoy the process!

8. Anything else you would love your audience to know or to know about you?

I've failed a lot. I want to quit all the time. It comes in waves. But when I feel like giving up, I try to zoom out and see my whole colorful journey as a living, breathing project. And then I feel like just being alive is an art form in itself. The lows make the highs shine that much brighter, and contrast is compelling.

Do you consider yourself an empath or highly sensitive person?

Yes.

www.bonniemckee.com
Instagram: @BonnieMckee
TikTok: @BonnieMckee

Angelo Kritikos

(He/Him)
Celebrity Photographer / Brand Owner

Angelo Kritikos is a celebrity photographer and music video director who is best known for his striking portraits and campaigns of top industry talent and brands. In 2022, Kritikos traveled the world on Demi Lovato's "HOLY FVCK" tour as the sole photographer and videographer, gaining him a 2023 iHeartRadio Music Award nomination for "FAVE TOUR PHOTOGRAPHER." He has shot for Demi Lovato, Billie Eilish, Normani, Nick Jonas, Gal Gadot, Rami Malek, and more.

1. Introduce yourself. Tell us who you are and what you do. Give us an overview of your career so far.

Hey, I'm Angelo! I'm a photographer and video director based in Los Angeles. I love creating and working with all artists. When I'm not touring or shooting on set, I am working on my genderless fragrance brand and other creative projects that bring me joy. I am a firm believer in doing what you love to do!

2. Tell us about your creative process. What works best for you? Have you experienced writer's block, imposter syndrome, procrastination, perfectionism, self-doubt, or self-limiting beliefs? How did you overcome them?

My creative process on a photography or music video set usually begins with me burning incense to cleanse the space. I start the day by bringing the entire crew and talent together for a motivational pep talk. I thank everyone for their creative energy and creating the space for a positive work environment. When I am working from home (editing, brand work, etc.) I will diffuse essential oils, burn incense, go on walks with my dog Moose and play music. Something I remind myself daily is 'done is better than perfect.' There are SO many people out there who have great ideas of starting projects but not many do the actual research, put in the time, get out of their comfort zone, and fully execute it. Any time I have limited beliefs about me or my work, I remind myself that I am doing what I love, and it will never be perfect, but at least I'm doing it. I am practicing finding joy in the process of creating, not the outcome of it.

3. If comfortable sharing, tell us how you've previously struggled with your mental health. (Have you experienced anxiety,

depression, a learning disability, ADHD, bipolar disorder? Or have you experienced adversity with your gender, sexuality, race?) What other challenges have you faced as a creative?

Absolutely. Growing up gay and very suppressed, I always felt and thought something was inherently wrong with me. I was so afraid of being gay that my brain created ways to keep me safe by distracting me from my reality. I would distract myself and punish myself with what I thought was a thousand times worse things than being gay (thoughts of death, freak accidents, etc.) I developed horrible intrusive thoughts and OCD that stuck with me for years and years. Instead of dealing with my reality of what was in front of me, I would have horrible anxiety and thoughts that were a thousand times scarier.

4. Tell us what you did (or continue to do) to cope with these challenges. Tell us some of the best strategies that have helped you overcome these struggles?

Therapy, therapy, therapy. As I grew older and became more accepting of who I was, I became self-aware that my old thought patterns and habits were no longer serving me, but my brain was hardwired as the scared little Angelo. I have always been a positive and bright person, but there was a darkness I was carrying with me anywhere I'd go. I became so exhausted from suffering with horrible anxiety I found a therapist and began my inner work. There were years before therapy that I would self-soothe my anxiety with meditations, working out, spiritual practices, etc. but it wasn't until I spoke with a proper medical professional my brain started to feel at ease again.

5. Are there any other art forms, hobbies, or interests you engage in to help restore your creative energy? What nurtures your soul? Any creative activities that recharge you?

I restore my creative energy by simply taking a break. Being near the ocean or in nature is very cleansing for my soul. I practice sustainability and daily wellness rituals on a day-to-day basis. I check in with myself daily to see what I intuitively need in that moment to bring me joy. Surrounding myself with loved ones, music, art, and my little treasures and objects recharge me.

6. What do you do for your self-care? Share any specific strategies, habits, or techniques that you find effective in improving your mental, emotional, physical, or spiritual self-care.

My self-care habits and rituals depend on the day. Some days self-care looks like a long shower or getting myself to the gym even if I don't want to. Other days, self-care is getting a massage or treating myself to something nice. I incorporate small daily rituals of self-care, which includes setting intentions, burning incense, and skin care.

7. What's one piece of self-care advice you would give to a person just starting out in a creative career?

Check in with yourself. Slow the fuck down. Ask yourself what would bring you joy in that moment.

www.angelokritikos.com
Instagram: @Angelokritikos
TikTok: @Kritikozzz

Kaydence

(She/Her)
Songwriter

Kaydence is a two time Grammy award-winning singer/songwriter based in Los Angeles. She cowrote Ariana Grande's No. one hit singles "Thank U, Next" and "7 Rings" and cowrote Beyoncé's "Black Parade," which won a Grammy for "Best R & B Performance" She has cowritten songs for Brandy, Daniel Caesar, Zayn, JLo, H.E.R, 6lack, Alina Baraz, Leon Bridges, and more.

1. Introduce yourself. Tell us who you are and what you do. Give us an overview of your career so far. (If possible, include some

career highs and lows.) Give us a brief description of what daily life looks like for you.

My name is Kaydence. I am a songwriter living in LA. I hit success in 2018, when I was able to write on Ariana Grande's *Sweetener* album, later leading me to work on her *Thank U, Next* album by cowriting, "Thank, U Next," "7 Rings," and more. Both songs charted number one on the Hot 100 billboard charts. Later on, I went on to cowrite, "Black Parade," for Beyoncé. While I've experienced the highs, I've also had to experience split disputes that resulted in a lot of strained relationships, not getting the credit I deserved, and experiencing what every songwriter has to go through: figuring out how to create stable income from an industry that is a huge financial gamble.

2. Tell us about your creative process. What works best for you? Have you experienced writer's block, imposter syndrome, procrastination, perfectionism, self-doubt, or self-limiting beliefs? How did you overcome them?

I've experienced imposter syndrome a lot. That ties into self-doubt and a lot of that comes from business experiences that made you question your worth. It's also being around such creative minds with impressive discography, so you are constantly comparing yourself. I overcame it by realizing we all experience it, and we all want to be accepted. As long as you remember that everyone is human and equal, and also that our music is all subjective, you start to put away the feelings of self-doubt and let yourself just be human too.

3. If comfortable sharing, tell us how you've previously struggled with your mental health. (Have you experienced anxiety, depression, a learning disability, ADHD, bipolar disorder? Or

have you experienced adversity with your gender, sexuality, race?) What other challenges have you faced as a creative?

I've experienced a lot of depression and ADHD and dealt with it throughout my career. I think most creatives all are, and that internal chaos comes out in the most beautiful ways through our music. It's honestly the most therapeutic method to express our feelings. Easier than expressing it in real life. Unfortunately, the business side of music can definitely contribute to depression if you let it. Still working on letting it affect me less.

4. Tell us what you did (or continue to do) to cope with these challenges. Tell us some of the best strategies that have helped you overcome these struggles.

Getting back to why you fell in love with music in the first place. The deeper you get into the business, the more your mind changes, and creates limitations on yourself. Being free creates breakthroughs in your mindset and your success.

5. Are there any other art forms, hobbies, or interests you engage in to help restore your creative energy? What nurtures your soul? Any creative activities that recharge you?

Experiencing real life outside the studio.

6. What do you do for your self-care? Share any specific strategies, habits, or techniques that you find effective in improving your mental, emotional, physical, or spiritual self-care.

There are memories from my childhood I reflect on. They call them "flashback moments" because they are core memories and affect your make-up and personality. I reflect on why those moments were so important and how they affect my decisions and actions in good and bad ways. When you're in tune with yourself, you can be in tune with the listeners.

7. What's one piece of self-care advice you would give to a person just starting out in a creative career?

Mind your business. Don't worry about what other people are doing; it will slow you down. You don't have to step on people to achieve success. Be a good person and let karma bless you later through your career and life.

Do you consider yourself an empath or highly sensitive person?

Yes.

Instagram: @Kaydence

Trey Campbell

(He/Him)
Songwriter/Vocal Producer/Executive Producer

Trey Campbell is a Grammy award-winning songwriter and vocal producer hailing from North Carolina. Trey has collaborated with Ellie Goulding, Giveon, Masego, Elley Duhey, Lola Young, John Legend, Mabel, Kaytranada, and Kim Petras. He has earned three Grammy nominations, two in the "Best R & B Album" category, and a nod in the "Best Reggae Album" category for his works on Giveon, John Legend, and Skip Marley. Trey cowrote "Gut Feeling" featuring HER on the Grammy award-winning artist, Ella Mai's debut No. one R & B album.

He has also cowritten songs for Lauren Jauregui, Amber Mark, Teddy Swims, Ingrid Andress, and Alina Baraz.

1. Introduce yourself. Tell us who you are and what you do. Give us an overview of your career so far. (If possible, include some career highs and lows.) Give us a brief description of what daily life looks like for you.

Hi, I'm Trey Campbell, a singer/songwriter/vocal producer based in Los Angeles. My day starts with meditation. I need a moment to center myself before I take on the day. Once centered, I usually answer emails while having breakfast. After breakfast, I do vocal warm-ups while showering. After showering, I usually do prep work for the day's session. Prep work involves listening to music for inspiration for the session. After prep work, it's session time. My sessions usually consist of an artist, a producer/production team, and myself.

2. Tell us about your creative process. What works best for you? Have you experienced writer's block, imposter syndrome, procrastination, perfectionism, self-doubt, or self-limiting beliefs? How did you overcome them?

When I'm collaborating, I love to start the session with casual conversation. I find that the real diamonds of truth are found when I'm connecting with the artist or producers. I feel like my primary job as a writer is to find the intersection between each of our life experiences. I'm constantly battling imposter syndrome and self-doubt because art is so subjective. One person could think your song is the greatest song they've ever heard, while another could not feel any connection to the song. I navigate the imposter syndrome and self-doubt by trusting the process. The truth always shows itself if you create a space for it to appear. I really try to be present and intentional, and that's really helped me navigate the seasons of the music industry.

3. If comfortable sharing, tell us how you've previously struggled with your mental health. (Have you experienced anxiety, depression, a learning disability, ADHD, bipolar disorder? Or have you experienced adversity with your gender, sexuality, race?) What other challenges have you faced as a creative?

I didn't really start experiencing anxiety and depression until I became a full-time songwriter. There is constant pressure to create songs that are commercially successful but not a lot of immediate financial support for the day-to-day task of songwriting. Most jobs, you're paid hourly, weekly, or monthly for your work. As a songwriter, your compensation is completely based upon the release and commercial success of the song. You can spend a majority of your day working on a song that may never be released. That means you will never be paid for that day's work. Being undervalued and poorly compensated makes you second-guess your worth.

I'm a gay black man. While the majority of the industry has been welcoming, there are still some spaces where I don't feel comfortable being my authentic self. For some people, perception and association is everything. Some heteronormative men are a bit guarded with me because I am open about my sexuality. It's hard to connect when you don't feel comfortable sharing your life experiences.

4. Tell us what you did (or continue to do) to cope with these challenges. Tell us some of the best strategies that have helped you overcome these struggles.

For me, it's important to meditate. I meditate to connect with myself. It's time for me to listen deeply to my intuition and my gut. It's time for me to check in with myself and make sure I'm good. I can't be great for others if I don't feel good about myself. I've also recently started exercising. Health is wealth. I always wanna present the best version of myself. When you feel good about yourself, people feel that. I've also found that people treat you better when you treat yourself better.

5. Are there any other art forms, hobbies, or interests you engage in to help restore your creative energy? What nurtures your soul? Any creative activities that recharge you?

I don't tell a lot of people this, but I like to dance. Sometimes when I feel stuck, I'll just put on an album and move around. Nothing super choreographed, just allowing my body to help my mind get unstuck. I know that the mathematical end of music is really important, but recently, I've started focusing on creating music that makes me wanna move. If it makes me wanna move, I think it'll make other people wanna move. Dancing helps me feel unstuck, and I hope that my music can help other people feel unstuck too.

6. What do you do for your self-care? Share any specific strategies, habits, or techniques that you find effective in improving your mental, emotional, physical, or spiritual self-care.

Meditation is key. When I'm really stressed, I try to get a massage. I get to shut my mind off and relax. Sometimes that break is the very thing I need to help me process my responsibilities. Belief in a higher power is very important to me. I attend an online church for inspirational messages. They uplift my spirit and remind me that I have a purpose on this earth.

7. What's one piece of self-care advice you would give to a person just starting out in a creative career?

One piece of self-care advice I would give to a person just starting out in a creative career is do the work. I know it's such a cliché phrase, but the sentiment is super important. Do the work to make sure you're mentally and physically healthy. The better you are, the better you can be with your collaborators. Do the work by studying and listening to music. The more versed you are in all genres of music, the more opportunities you create for yourself. Do the work of putting in your ten thousand hours. Honestly, for some of us it's one million hours, but don't be discouraged by that. Roll up your sleeves and get your hands dirty because you might be surprised by what you find when you dig deep.

8. Anything else you would love your audience to know or to know about you?
The best is yet to come!!!

Do you consider yourself an empath or highly sensitive person?
Yes.

Instagram: @treycampbellmusic

Jessa Doll

(She/Her)
Movement Coach, Choreographer, Professional Dancer

Jessa Doll is a professional dancer from Vancouver, Canada, now based in Los Angeles. She has toured the world with Maluma and worked with artists such as Ariana Grande, Jennifer Lopez, French Montana, Natalie La Rose, Loote, Jeremih, Jesse McCartney, Marianas Trench, and Michael Buble. She has also appeared as a dancer in numerous television series like *Grease: Rise of the Pink Ladies, Riverdale, DC Legends of Tomorrow, Chilling Adventures of Sabrina* and more. She is the creator of Doll in Motion, a movement coaching company that has worked with artists such as Gia Woods, DYLN, Bava, Julia Wolf, Jessie

Chambers, Rohan, Love Fame Tragedy, Maxyme, and Amanda Frances.

1. Introduce yourself. Tell us who you are and what you do. Give us an overview of your career so far. (If possible, include some career highs and lows.) Give us a brief description of what daily life looks like for you.

Hello! My name is Jessa Doll and I am a movement coach, choreographer, and professional dancer. I am originally from Vancouver, Canada but reside in Los Angeles. I have lived in LA for nine years. I first moved out here as a dancer starry eyed for LA. My first few years in LA involved a lot of interesting side gigs and trial and error moments. It wasn't until my fifth year that I hit my "big break" when I was hired to dance on tour for Latin artist Maluma, traveling all over the world performing with him in sold-out arenas such as Madison Square Garden and The Forum. Right before that big break, I actually moved back to Canada for about five months, convinced it wasn't in the cards for me.

After those five months I said, "Let's give it one last go." I changed my look (hair color) and moved back. Within the first month, I booked my first awards show, booked two music videos with A-list artists, and shortly after booked the tour. It truly taught me resilience is key. After being on the road for almost three years, I am now back in Los Angeles still pursuing dance but now fully pursuing my other passions, which are movement coaching and choreography. Daily life for me looks like waking up with my morning coffee and music, computer work, going for a nice beach walk while listening to a podcast, and making sure my apartment is organized. (Those are my constants.) Throughout the week it varies work wise (Ex: Studio sessions/teaching/dance jobs/auditions or taking dance class.) I try to use at least one day on the weekend to fully disconnect from work and limit my social media use.

2. Tell us about your creative process. What works best for you? Have you experienced writer's block, imposter syndrome, procrastination, perfectionism, self-doubt, or self-limiting beliefs? How did you overcome them?

My creative process varies depending on the project. When I work with artists, I always listen to the song first and see what initially comes to my mind. I am a very visual person and can often see a greater picture or what it could potentially look like. I'll make sure to research the artists' platforms, past performances, and music videos so I can get a general feel for their vibe and energy. I'll then have a discussion with the artist or client and see what their vision/needs/goals are and then find a way I can collaborate the two together! My goal is to always create something that is unique and authentic to the artist that makes them feel confident and powerful. I'm definitely a perfectionist at heart but like to think I have a healthy dose of it. If anything, I struggle most with my overthinking. I find myself often going down rabbit holes of unrealistic circumstances. I think because I have had a few really weird, one-of-a-kind scenarios happen, it's easy to believe, "If it's going to happen to anyone, it's me," or "Well, it happened that one time." The best way I've found to cope with that is as soon as I feel myself spiraling, switch to a different activity, challenge the belief, and play worst-case, best-case scenario. It's something I'm still working on, but I believe if one can get to a place of balancing perfectionism and overthinking, it can have positive effects like being self-aware and creating thorough elevated work.

3. If comfortable sharing, tell us how you've previously struggled with your mental health. (Have you experienced anxiety,

SELF-CARE FOR THE CREATIVE

depression, a learning disability, ADHD, bipolar disorder? Or have you experienced adversity with your gender, sexuality, race?) What other challenges have you faced as a creative?

I have struggled and still do with anxiety. The entertainment industry is full of so many unknowns on a day-to-day basis; it's something that is just always there. I've joked around with people before saying that showing up to auditions or dance jobs is like showing up for your first day on a new job every day. You don't know if you'll know anyone, what you'll be doing, a new location from project to project. Just a huge question mark daily, which can be unsettling.

4. Tell us what you did (or continue to do) to cope with these challenges. Tell us some of the best strategies that have helped you overcome these struggles.

Actively choosing and adopting a positive, carefree attitude has helped me a lot recently. I've found when I'm proactively choosing things that are good for me (ex: podcasts, reading, eating healthy, staying organized, other activities that are creative that don't have to do with dance, etc.), I find myself in a better headspace. At first it felt like a chore and left me wondering if it would really help. But after a short period of time, it became a part of my routine, and I can feel it all naturally having a positive effect on my system and helping with my anxiety. I've also learnt some very simple techniques from a therapist and life coach that have helped. For example, when things get stressful, I say to myself, "Oh well." Ha! It's simple, takes the pressure off the scenario, and puts it into perspective. Also, little pep talks to myself and my inner child help as well. :)

5. Are there any other art forms, hobbies, or interests you engage in to help restore your creative energy? What nurtures your soul? Any creative activities that recharge you?

I love anything arts/crafts. I went through a phase where I loved flipping worn down furniture I would find. I also enjoy thrift store/garage sale hunting. There's something about finding hidden gems that puts a huge smile on my face. Apart from those things, I find any activity in nature really recharges and grounds me.

6. What do you do for your self-care? Share any specific strategies, habits, or techniques that you find effective in improving your mental, emotional, physical, or spiritual self-care.

As simple as it is, I love doing my skin care routine, something about it calms and relaxes me. I recently started using *The Five Minute Journal*, which has been such a positive tool. It helps me sort through my thoughts, find the positives, and practice gratitude at the beginning and end of each day. I also try really hard to be active outside of dance, even if it's just a fifteen minute walk. I think balance is so important. There is no way you can operate at your one hundred if you're in a constant headspace of hustle and work. There has to be some fun and relaxation in there, whatever that may be.

7. What's one piece of self-care advice you would give to a person just starting out in a creative career?

Be gentle with yourself, it's all trial and error and a learning experience. It's honestly weird if you don't make mistakes, so just embrace it and grow.

jessadoll.wixsite.com/jessadoll
Instagram: @JessicaDoll
Instagram: @DollinMotion

Tina Maria Elena

(She/Her)
Artist

Danish/French artist Tina Maria Elena holds the female gaze as paramount in the articulation of her creative vision. She specializes in watercolor works that explore the sensual nature of love and the female form. She has over 380k followers on Instagram (@tinamariaelena) and has exhibited her works in Denmark and the US. Web shop: www.tinamariaelena.com

1. Introduce yourself. Tell us who you are and what you do. Give us an overview of your career so far. (If possible, include some

career highs and lows.) Give us a brief description of what daily life looks like for you.

My name is Tina Maria Elena Bak and I'm a thirty-eight-year-old artist living and working in Odense, Denmark. I'm married, and my mother is Danish and my father is French. At the age of six, I proclaimed that I wanted to become an artist when I grew up. And although I later on gave up on the idea of going to art school (without even trying), this feeling and wish never abandoned me. After I had twins in 2010, I became really creative again. It was a way for me to relax, and I felt a great need to use my artistic skills as an outlet for all of my feelings. My son is disabled both physically and mentally and needs a lot of care. I definitely chose to shift my creative energy directly into something beautiful and filled with power and love, and that's where my journey of sensual art began. This journey led to my Make Love Watercolor paintings, which started in April 2016. And this series opened the doors to many of my other series. My daily life is a mix of working with my art, shipping orders from my web shop, and taking care of my son and daughter, of course.

2. Tell us about your creative process. What works best for you? Have you experienced writer's block, imposter syndrome, procrastination, perfectionism, self-doubt, or self-limiting beliefs? How did you overcome them?

Usually I get my inspiration from various mediums. A picture, very often music I listen to, a beautiful sunset, or something I read—or even personal feelings/experiences. My process often starts with a sketch of the image I wish to paint. When I'm happy with my sketch, I start painting. I often have self-doubt, but it's a shift between feeling on top of the world and sometimes afterwards not thinking the painting is good enough. Mostly though, I am satisfied with the finished painting. I'm usually very inspired, but there's of course times where I feel tired, unin-spired, or even start to worry that my "fake-it-till-you-make-it" will be discovered, so that's a clear symptom of imposter syn-drome. If I have these annoying feelings, I simply take a break from creating, and sometimes it helps to take a look back at all I have created, so that I can remind myself that I have a mission and a talent.

3. If comfortable sharing, tell us how you've previously strug-gled with your mental health. (Have you experienced anxiety, depression, a learning disability, ADHD, bipolar disorder? Or have you experienced adversity with your gender, sexuality, race?) What other challenges have you faced as a creative?

When I was about eighteen, I think I had an undiagnosed depression. And when I was about thirty-three years old, I had a meltdown. I was burnt out with stress. And I had some huge anxiety attacks. From then on, I sadly have developed anxiety, a form that has stayed and that I have to deal with almost daily. It helps when I can soothe my mind and stop the almost endless thoughts and worries. I am an overthinker. I have gone to ther-apy and that helps.

4. Tell us what you did (or continue to do) to cope with these challenges. Tell us some of the best strategies that have helped you overcome these struggles.

It helps me to put my thoughts to a pause. When I paint, I only focus on the work and the music I listen to. And it also helps to listen to funny or interesting podcasts when I go for a walk, for example. When it's too quiet, I tend to worry more. But overall, I think therapy has been the best way to move for-ward and try to let go of past traumas.

5. Are there any other art forms, hobbies, or interests you engage in to help restore your creative energy? What nurtures your soul? Any creative activities that recharge you?

It nurtures my soul to draw and paint, but also sometimes to sing and dance/use my body. I used to sing a lot. Now I only sing alone. It has become private.

6. What do you do for your self-care? Share any specific strategies, habits, or techniques that you find effective in improving your mental, emotional, physical, or spiritual self-care.

When I started my "Make Love" series, I felt empowered by my own work. I felt like I could let go of my worries (for a while), and I felt as beautiful and sensual as my art. I was longing for this comfortable feeling in my own skin and my hope is that my art, for example, my "Self Love" series, can lead others to have more gentle eyes on ourselves and less judgment. Whenever I feel stressed out, I try to slow down and make some to-do lists when the day becomes overwhelming. It helps, even though I don't complete the list. But it helps me prioritize the list of things I need to do. Remember that self-punishment never leads to self-love.

7. What's one piece of self-care advice you would give to a person just starting out in a creative career?

It is really a cliché but do not compare yourself and your art too much to other artists and their work. You do you. Also, enjoy that you have something special that makes you stand out. Also, if it's something a bit quirky and weird, that's just fun and interesting. And it's okay to shift direction in your work. No one stays the same or enjoys becoming an echo of themselves forever.

8. Anything else you would love your audience to know or to know about you?

It's not about making extraordinary pieces all the time. It's about keeping the creative flow and passion for what you love and to express that through your art.

www.tinamariaelena.com
Instagram: @tinamariaelena
Tiktok: @tinamariaelena

Jenna Andrews

Songwriter

Jenna Andrews is an executive producer, artist, songwriter, and vocal producer. She's cowritten songs such as BTS's No. one hit song, "Butter," "Supalonley" by Benee, and "Heartbreak Anthem" by Galantis with David Guetta and Little Mix. She is the owner of the publishing company Twenty Seven Music, which is home to Mike Sonier, Little Mix, 44 phantom, and more. She is the host of the podcast "The Green Room Talks," which discusses issues surrounding mental health, featuring guests such as Tegan and Sara, Lennon Stella, JoJo, Mickey Guyton, and Dixie D'Amelio, to name a few.

1. Introduce yourself. Tell us who you are and what you do. Give us an overview of your career so far. (If possible, include some career highs and lows.) Give us a brief description of what daily life looks like for you.

My daily life really depends, but between all the different things I do, there is never a dull moment. Getting signed and dropped was definitely a high and low moment. It was a really good learning experience to never get too high or too low and to not ever give up on your dream. Being in the music industry is a constant fight with downfalls and rewards at every turn.

2. Tell us about your creative process. What works best for you? Have you experienced writer's block, imposter syndrome, procrastination, perfectionism, self-doubt, or self-limiting beliefs? How did you overcome them?

I would say that I have experienced all of this. I think these are things that never truly go away, but it's finding ways to be able to cope and use weaknesses as strengths.

3. If comfortable sharing, tell us how you've previously struggled with your mental health. (Have you experienced anxiety, depression, a learning disability, ADHD, bipolar disorder? Or have you experienced adversity with your gender, sexuality, race?) What other challenges have you faced as a creative?

I have really bad anxiety. It's why I wanted to start a podcast talking about it openly because I find the ability to share vulnerable moments with other people going through the same thing or a similar thing is a very cathartic experience.

4. Tell us what you did (or continue to do) to cope with these challenges. Tell us some of the best strategies that have helped you overcome these struggles.

For me it is talking about it openly and not feeling ashamed. I feel like it breaks the barrier when getting to know someone or even while writing a song.

5. Are there any other art forms, hobbies, or interests you engage in to help restore your creative energy? What nurtures your soul? Any creative activities that recharge you?
I love fashion, cooking, and doing my mental health podcast.

6. What do you do for your self-care? Share any specific strategies, habits, or techniques that you find effective in improving your mental, emotional, physical, or spiritual self-care.
Spending time with my dogs makes me feel better. Not taking life too seriously and taking time off when I feel like I need it and not feeling guilty about it.

7. What's one piece of self-care advice you would give to a person just starting out in a creative career?
Authenticity is very freeing.

Do you consider yourself an empath or highly sensitive person?
Yes.

Instagram: @thejennaandrews
TikTok: @thejennaandrews

Jesse Thomas

(She/her)
Artist/Songwriter

Jesse Thomas is an artist and songwriter who curates and hosts Jesse and Friends, a popular songwriter showcase. She has over one billion streams, and her writing has been on three separate Grammy nominated albums. She cowrote Martin Garrix and Troye Sivan's platinum hit, "There for You," as well as songs with Kelly Clarkson, Chris Stapleton, Donna Missal, Ben Platt, PTX, Royal and The Serpent, Cailin Russo, Charlotte Lawrence, Ingrid Michaelson, Ingrid Andress, Wrabel, and more.

1. Introduce yourself. Tell us who you are and what you do. Give us an overview of your career so far. (If possible, include some career highs and lows.) Give us a brief description of what daily life looks like for you.

I am a professional songwriter and showcase curator. I moved to Los Angeles fifteen years ago to be an actor and stand-up comedian. I fell into music; that was only a hobby. I played some open mics and got linked up with a producer, who I ended up working with for eight years. I released a few albums and EPs as an artist. I had some great moments, but my career never really caught on. I switched gears to songwriting for other people, and for a while, I retired from my artist project. It took me a few years to rebuild my community and to meet the right people, but eventually, I had an impressive folder of pitch songs. My friend Wrabel helped get my songs to some key people, and I eventually landed a publishing deal with Warner Chappell. I was suddenly working with some of the biggest names in the business, and even got a big cut with Martin Garrix within my first few months of being signed. It's been seven years, and even though I still feel like I struggle, if I step back and look at everything I've done, I'm really proud of myself. Three Grammy nominations, collabs with people from all over the world, a few platinum records, and most importantly, the simple blessing of getting to do this every day. I've had to reinvent the way I write music over the years, and that is one of my favorite parts about it. I am still out here grindin' seven years later, chasing beautiful music.

2. Tell us about your creative process. What works best for you? Have you experienced writer's block, imposter syndrome, procrastination, perfectionism, self-doubt, or self-limiting beliefs? How did you overcome them?

Recently I've been trying to stay out of my way as much as possible. My best ideas usually come from not thinking about them too much. Little gifts from the universe. Those nuggets seem to come when I'm not trying very hard, and I'm just having fun vibing. Sometimes I get really uninspired. I don't get too wrapped up in that anymore. It's part of the process. I've done a lot of work to believe in and love myself and am just now finding my groove with that as a creator. In sessions, I lie on the floor, close my eyes, and try to clear my mind and wait for the lyric to move through me. I believe if I can keep my channel clear, the universe will send me beautiful gifts. I think the only art worth making is honest art, so my main focus is to put as much of myself as possible into what I am making. It's kinda woo-woo, and I used to not always write like this, but it is what has given me the most results.

3. If comfortable sharing, tell us how you've previously struggled with your mental health. (Have you experienced anxiety, depression, a learning disability, ADHD, bipolar disorder? Or have you experienced adversity with your gender, sexuality, race?) What other challenges have you faced as a creative?

I've never been diagnosed with anything, but I believe I struggle with OCD, ADHD, anxiety, and depression. I don't remember much of my childhood. I grew up gay in Kentucky and experienced a lot of disassociation and rejection when I was younger. I felt weird my whole life and moved to Los Angeles as soon as I could. Being in the closet is horrible and I didn't come out until my late 20s. Finding music and other queer people in the city helped me figure out who I am. I've found pride in my uniqueness and leaning into it has helped my songwriting immensely. My healing journey has been a long one, but I feel I am finally in a place where I am getting better every day.

4. Tell us what you did (or continue to do) to cope with these challenges. Tell us some of the best strategies that have helped you overcome these struggles?

I've used marijuana to cope. It is something I found that calms me down and helps me focus. In my experience, mushrooms and ayahuasca are incredible. Like years of therapy in a few hours. I do hot yoga, meditate, eat organic, drink sourced water, and just took up ceramics! I'm working less, but with more intent. Studying consciousness and human history helps me see the beauty of this life and take things less seriously. I am a big believer in reading books and meditating. It has changed my life immensely, and I will continue using those tools to help assist my healing journey.

5. Are there any other art forms, hobbies, or interests you engage in to help restore your creative energy? What nurtures your soul? Any creative activities that recharge you?

Spending time in nature and with my dog. Walking barefoot. I take a twenty-minute barefoot walk every morning to ground myself. Grounding is a free technique that has a lot of health benefits! I like to be outside, around water and nature. Traveling. Dancing. Kissing. I go dancing a lot—that is key.

6. What do you do for your self-care? Share any specific strategies, habits, or techniques that you find effective in improving your mental, emotional, physical, or spiritual self-care.

I protect my energy. I keep my circle small. I keep my house clean. I take long showers and do breath work. I meditate, journal, read, smoke weed, do mushrooms, and yoga. I also use crystals!

7. What's one piece of self-care advice you would give to a person just starting out in a creative career?

Be yourself. It's so simple, but it's one of the hardest things to be. I could have saved myself a lot of time if I had focused on loving and trusting myself, instead of trying to be someone I wasn't.

8. Anything else you would love your audience to know or to know about you?
Check out my music project Thomboi and have a nice day!

Do you consider yourself an empath or highly sensitive person?
Yes.

Instagram: @jesse.and.friends @jessethomas____
Tiktok: @jesse.and.friends @thomboi___

About the Author

Stefani Fryzel (aka DYLN) has spent two decades in the music industry as an artist, songwriter, and music producer. Her work has been nominated for a Grammy, featured on the Billboard Charts, nominated for radio music awards, and appeared in film and television. She is the creator of "The Songwriter Series," an online event that offers 1:1 music mentorship from award-winning hit songwriters and is the host of "Self-Care for the Creative," a podcast that discusses self-care strategies for people in creative communities. She lives in Los Angeles.

www.stefanifryzel.com
Instagram: @stefanifryzel
Tiktok: @stefanifryzel

Works Cited

Warrier, Varun. "Study Finds that Genes Play a Role in Empathy." *University of Cambridge*. 12 Mar. 2018. https://www.cam.ac.uk/research/news/study-finds-that-genes-play-a-role-in-empathy#. Accessed 27 Apr. 2023.

Resources

Books

Aron, Elaine N. *The Highly Sensitive Person.*
Beattie, Melody. *Codependent No More.*
Cameron, Julia. *The Artist's Way.*
Connell, Sara. *The Science of Getting Rich for Women.*
Dyer, Judy. *Empath.*
—. *The Empowered Empath.*
Gobin, Robyn L. *The Self-Care Prescription.*
Hiscock, Arin Murphy. *The Green Witch.*
—. *The Witch's Book of Self-Care.*
Orloff, Judith. *The Empath's Survival Guide.*
Sarkis, Stephanie Moulton. *Healing From Toxic Relationships.*
Sincero, Jen. *You Are a Badass.*

Hotlines

988 SUICIDE AND CRISIS LIFELINE Call or Text 988
The Lifeline provides 24/7, free and confidential support for people in distress, prevention and crisis resources for you or your loved ones, and best practices for professionals in the United States. Call or Text 988
www.988lifeline.org

NATIONAL ALLIANCE ON MENTAL ILLNESS (NAMI) Call 1-800-950-NAMI (6264)
NAMI provides advocacy, education, support and public

awareness so that all individuals and families affected by mental illness can build better lives.

The NAMI HelpLine can be reached Monday through Friday, 10 a.m. – 10 p.m., ET.

Call 1-800-950-NAMI (6264), text "HelpLine" to 62640 or email us at helpline@nami.org

www.nami.org

SAMHSA NATIONAL HELPLINE Call 1-800-662-HELP (4357)
Substance Abuse and Mental Health Services Administration National Helpline is a free, confidential, 24/7, 365-day-a-year treatment referral and information service for individuals and families facing mental and/or substance use disorders. For a referral for mental health treatment, call 1-800-662-HELP

www.samhsa.gov

THE JED FOUNDATION call 1800-273-TALK (8255)
If you or someone you know needs to talk to someone right now, text HOME to 741-741 or call 1800-273-TALK (8255) for a free confidential conversation with a trained counselor 24/7. www.jedfoundation.org

NATIONAL EATING DISORDERS ASSOCIATION (NEDA) HELPLINE Call 1-800-931-2237
If you or a loved one is suffering from an eating disorder, there are a breadth of hotlines that you may contact. The NEDA has various options, including online chatting, calling, or even texting. If you are unable to reach someone immediately, you can always leave a message or text "NEDA" to 741741, which will connect you to an individual at a Crisis Text Line. www.nationaleatingdisorders.org

NATIONAL DOMESTIC VIOLENCE HOTLINE Call 1-800-799-7233
24 hours a day, seven days a week, 365 days a year, the National Domestic Violence Hotline provides essential tools and support to help survivors of domestic violence so they can live their lives free of abuse. National Domestic Violence Hotline: Call 1-800-799-SAFE (7233), chat online, or text START to 88788 www.thehotline.org

Connect with a Therapist

BETTERHELP
Betterhelp is a mental health platform that provides mental health services directly to consumers. The online counseling and therapy services are provided through web-based interaction as well as phone and text communication. www.betterhelp.com

TALKSPACE
An online and mobile therapy company. Support your mental health with the support from a licensed therapist. www.talkspace.com

TELADOC
A virtual healthcare company. Get healthcare online from doctors, therapists, specialists, and more via phone or video for fast, convenient, high-quality care, anytime, anywhere. www.teledoc.com

Podcasts

THE NARCISSISTIC ABUSE AND TRAUMA RECOVERY PODCAST by Caroline Strawson

The Narcissistic Abuse and Trauma Recovery Podcast is to help women thrive after the devastating effects from the trauma of narcissistic abuse. Hosted by Caroline Strawson, bestselling author, speaker and award-winning Trauma Therapist and Coach and founder of the No. one Trauma Informed Narcissistic Trauma Recovery Programme.

Sleep Hypnosis and Guided Meditations

MICHAEL SEALEY
Hypnosis, hypnotherapy, sleep meditation, and guided meditation recordings available on YouTube and Spotify.

Meditation Techniques

TRANSCENDENTAL MEDITATION (TM)
Transcendental Meditation is a form of silent mantra meditation. The TM technique involves the use of a silently used sound called mantra, and is practiced for fifteen to twenty minutes twice per day.
www.tm.org

Manufactured by Amazon.ca
Bolton, ON

35858741R00203